Butterflies Don't I

by Jay (

Barbara,

Best Wishes.

Jay Carter

To my beautiful wife, Sheila.

Butterflies Don't Land on Manure

Copyright ©1998 by

Unicorn Press
P.O. Box 6048
Wyomissing, PA 19610
529 Reading Ave., Suite M, West Reading, PA 19611

Cover design by:
Flora Po Cusimano
421 Rugby Rd.
Birdsboro, PA 19508

Edited by Margaret Verhulst, Ph.D.
Patricia Kramer, BSNA
Illustrations by WordPerfect Corp.
Reviewed by and thanks to Michael Constantine

Introduction

Once upon a time, in this very land, there was a man who learned everything in this book ... and died. He was transformed, and in any transformation, the "caterpillar" dies. So you might think twice before reading any further. This is the story of the transformation of Jack Callahan. Transformation was a necessary and essential process that allowed Jack to find himself, and then find true love. It is exactly the sort of transformation that occurs when a caterpillar becomes a butterfly, in that it can't be changed back. The caterpillar dies so the butterfly can be born. If chosen, it is a one way trip. Now that I have warned you, I will make no apologies for what happens.

Along the journey of a transformation, the transformee usually meets with dragons and wizards. Of course, in this day and age, a dragon no longer <u>looks</u> like a dragon and a wizard no longer <u>looks</u> like a wizard. That makes the journey more difficult, and perhaps more interesting. A dragon today, may take on the form of a beautiful woman. And instead of breathing fire overtly, may just create a fire in the opponent in the form of sex, an ulcer, or anxiety. A wizard, as eccentric as they are, may take on any form. Say, for example, the form of an air-headed blonde from Brooklyn. Then the trick would be to avoid the cunning beautiful dragon who lights the fires, and listen to the eccentric friend. The dragon may appear confident (actually it is arrogant and has a sense of entitlement), while the friend may appear to be a little different. But the difference is that the dragon is ... self-serving.

Jack traveled the world for IPM. He seemed to have everything: a good job, a beautiful wife, a dog, a cat, and a dream house in the suburbs. But he was not happy.

The fuzzy caterpillar
Walked the sidewalk
With all the other
Fuzzy caterpillars,
Alone.

Jay Carter

He was hungry.
He ate and ate
And nothing would
Fill him up.

One day,
He stopped eating,
And looked around.
It wasn't working.

So, he built
A cocoon around him
And waited
To die.

The spirit of a butterfly
Touched his cocoon,
And he wept
With the beauty of it
And caterpillar Jack died.

Later, with the spirit
Of a butterfly
He awoke,
And went to find her.

Then, with the eyes
Of a butterfly,
He saw her
And felt real.

And with the wings
Of a butterfly,
He flew to her
And stayed with her,
Together ... forever.

Follow fuzzy Jack through the moments of truth that led to the end of his old life - or identity - as he knew it: through the discovery of his true self, the discovery of true love, and the beginning of a new life.

* A transformation for a human being is a significant shift in perspective. It is when a human finally "sees", without the limits of the eyes or mind, but discovers what has been there all along. A human being in the caterpillar stage could be likened to ... an eye looking for itself.

A transformation is not a fleeting "high". Rather, it is the simplest, foremost, unintense, and most meaningful acknowledgement of one's existence that one can have. It is a "yes" experience. Not a loud yes, a racy yes, or a giddy yes, but a simple and deeply profound one. It is the alignment of the soul with its purpose and what is. It is when the old identity quietly dies, the real self is born.

Some old caterpillar habits may follow this person through the transformation, but will eventually disappear. The person may still chew on a leaf or two, but leaves will not taste good, anymore. He/she will be more attracted to nectar. He/she may sometimes walk with legs, but the preference to soar peacefully through the sky will be dominant. And with these discoveries comes the sacred knowledge that within every human caterpillar, there is a butterfly. You can't drag a caterpillar, kicking and screaming, through a transformation. The transformation must be a conscious choice on the part of the caterpillar, and the caterpillar has to be ready. The caterpillar is the only one who can make the cocoon. It is fearsome, because the caterpillar must die before the butterfly can be born.

But, whereas a caterpillar may step in manure, a butterfly does not.

Dad

Just after Christmas in 1984, Jack's dad, Frank Callahan, lay in his hospital bed. The old guy looked fairly alive, for a man who was dying. Even though his skin color was a pale pasty white and his hair more white than grey, his dry lips could still create a smile that would animate even the sickest body. His wife Betty sat at his bedside. She was her usual gracious, kind self, gently inviting Jack and his sister to step closer to the bed. They appeared a little awkward in front of her, since they were his children from his first marriage of fifteen years. He was their father and the only father-figure they had known. Betty had been "the other woman", but to her credit, she had always maintained a quiet dignity in the face of criticism. At this moment, in keeping with her character, she made up an excuse about going to get something to eat so she could leave the father and his children alone together.

Sharon had been Daddy's little girl and was very close with him in an affectionate way. She was now 35, and although she was not strikingly beautiful, she carried herself with confidence and grace. Her blue eyes, tasselled blonde hair, and quick smile gave her a warm friendly appearance. She was happily married with two kids - a classic mother and housewife.

Jack was his father's first born, three years older than Sharon. He had shared the same interests with his Dad and was like him in many ways, even physically. He was just under six feet tall, with sandy hair turning grey, blue eyes, and a semi-macho look. He hadn't been happy in his marriage with Lynn since the beginning, and he had become a man with a heavy burden on his shoulders.

Frank Callahan had suffered three heart attacks that week, and three times he had successfully cheated death, but his heart was so damaged that the doctors said he could go at any time. The old man knew he was not long for this world but he had held on to see his children one last time, to say goodbye.

As Betty left the room, Sharon hurried to her father's side and took his hand. She let the tears stream down her face and said, "I love you, Dad."

"I love you, too, Pumpkin," he replied.

Jack approached the bed and reassuringly patted his father's shoulder. "You're going to be OK, Dad."

The old man looked warmly at his denial stricken son. He said, "You know Jack, I've come to realize you are just like me. You probably think I am going to live through this and you'll see me tomorrow, but I think we had better make the most of this moment."

"OK, Dad." Jack sighed, his denial punctured.

The old man looked at his son, as if for a life time. He looked down past the man part of him into the little boy part. Then he said, "Remember, Jack, when you were five years old and we would play 'let's pretend'?"

"Sure I do, Dad."

"Well, I want to play that with you just one more time."

Jack looked around the room quickly and said, "You mean **now?!**"

"All we ever have is **now**," said the old man, smiling. "And, I get to go first."

"Sure, Dad. Anything you say."

"OK. I want you to pretend I'm dying, and that you will never see me again after tonight. Just in case, you know, this **is** it, I don't want you to miss out on the experience."

"OK, Dad."

Frank looked Jack straight in the eyes with a no-nonsense look. "I'm not finished yet. I want you to also pretend you are five years old again, and you hadn't yet matured into a man who could hide his feelings and keep himself so damn collected."

Jack could feel the lump in his throat and was trying very hard to maintain his composure.

The old man reached out to his son and beckoned. He said throatily, "Just be my little boy again .. just for a little while."

From the bottom of Jack's soul came a little boy's sob that

even his manly vocal chords could not hold back. He slowly put his head on his father's chest and held onto him like a child. He didn't want to let his father go. His father ran his hand through Jack's hair and said, "You're a good boy Jack. Thanks for trying to be strong for me. I love you, son." Jack heaved with tears of sadness, knowing he would soon lose his father. It felt good to be a child again. After a few moments, he stood up, slowly regaining his composure.

The old man laughed and tactfully joked about living to see Jack finally lose his cool. He said he hoped his son would have a better time at his funeral.

Sharon tried to lighten things up by telling her dad what had happened to "Cool Hand Jack" at her home earlier. The neighbor's dog had left a "present" on her sidewalk. Jack avoided it when he came into the house, but on the way out, he stepped on one of the kid's little cars and danced down the steps almost losing his balance. Just when he thought he had made it, he looked back at Sharon, giving her a smug look and stepped right in the "present". Sharon squealed with laughter. Frank looked at his son to see this embarrassed grin and chuckled that old familiar chuckle that always seemed to make everything OK. He thanked his children for all the happiness they had given him and for some of the finest moments in his life. The room became a whirlwind of memories. They reminisced about the good times and joked about the bad. When Jack asked what he could do for him, the old man answered, "You know Jack, we men always want to **do** something when sometimes there's nothing to **do**. Be happy in your life, Jack. That's what you can do for me."

It seemed as if they were there forever, and paradoxically, it seemed it was a just a short time. Before they knew it, visiting hours were over. Betty returned to the room just after the door shut behind Frank's children. The tired old man looked over at his wife. She was smiling at him in her usual loving way. They didn't need to speak, just savor this moment together as they had savored many other moments.

Later, he would turn to his wife and say, "It is my dying

wish that my children be as happy as we are."

It was during that night sometime that he died in Betty's gentle loving arms.

Jack and Sharon had never allowed themselves to like Betty. She had been, after all, "the other woman". Jack had always been coldly civil to Betty. Sharon had been overtly uncivil. But over the years, Jack had come to understand some of the complications of life, and he knew his father had been happy with Betty. Consequently, at the end of the traditional funeral service, he sought Betty out. He caught her gently by her forearm and turned her around. He looked at her differently now, intently, as if for the first time. His father had found love and peace with her. "Thank you," he said earnestly.

She knew what he meant and smiled. "Be happy in your life, Jack," she said, with an intense sincerity. They looked at each other for a moment more, as they had just given each other a most precious gift. But that spiritual moment was interrupted rudely by the scolding voice of Jack's wife, Lynn.

"Jaack!" she said
impatiently. As usual, Lynn
was decked out in the most
appropriate dress. She wore
her dark brown hair up in
an aristocratic looking style.
Her slim but well-endowed
body always drew stares from the older men.
"Coming," he said. He smiled sheepishly at Betty.
"Go on," she said.

Jack got into his Honda with Lynn. As they drove away, Lynn "reminded" him that his mother was waiting for him. She reprimanded him, saying that people might think he was being disloyal to his mother by talking to "that woman". Later, on the drive home, she chided him for seeking "that woman" out. She said it was almost like condoning the breakup of his parents' marriage. Jack's stomach twisted with the usual anxiety. He remembered his parent's breakup. He was 15 when his father left. He had felt a sense of relief because his parents had been fighting daily.

Jack had always been his mother's favorite. Lenora had put all of her energies into Jack and withdrew from his father. His father was never good enough. She would tell Jack what a bastard his father was and point out all of his faults. She would constantly say, "You are not going to be like him, Jack. You are going to be good to your wife, I know." Jack listened to her and took her side. He strove **not** to be like his father. The ultimate insult to him was when she would say, "You are just like your father!" Consequently, when he was younger, Jack did not have much use for his father.

But in recent years, Jack had come to appreciate his father and maybe even understand why he had left. Try as he might, Jack could never seem to be good enough for his own wife. He glanced at her as they drove. She looked exceedingly perturbed, as usual. He got the feeling that she was always disappointed in him... that he never quite measured up to her expectations. He wondered why she stayed with him. After all, Lynn's parents were from the Main Line in Philadelphia and her father was a millionaire. Sure, they thought he was a nice enough guy, but he had come from the poor side of town and not from their high social stratum. They thought their daughter could have done better.

Jack's father was a bright man who grew up on a farm and was a farmer at heart. He had left farming when Jack was ten years old to work as an electrician (self taught) under the pressure of Jack's mother, who was tired of being a poor farm wife. Jack's mother had grown up in a well educated family. Her family had been, at one time, very well off, but had lost a retail business in the depression. She had the demeanor and social graces of an upper class woman, but lacked the financial resources to live a socialite's life.

More and more, Jack understood why his father had left his mother. One thing he had realized in recent years was that his dad had **never** said anything derogatory about his mother ...

and there **were** things he could have said! She was no saint and could be extremely difficult to live with, always blaming Frank for their misfortunes. But she had worshipped her only son and he had always felt special. Now Jack realized that she had put all of her energies into him to the <u>exclusion</u> of his father. It is a wonder his dad had not been more jealous or even resented him. Jack had come to realize that his mother had actually alienated him from his father. He had more respect for his father now that he was older and able to step back from the situation. He was glad that he had spent more time with his father in the past several years. It made him feel more complete and brought a smile to his face.

Of course, his dad had matured over the years, but Jack remembered one time he tried to ask his dad about women. It was May 20, 1960. (Jack remembered because it was the "birthday" of his first car. His uncle had given him a clunker to work on). At 15, Jack had a dream in which he was lying by a tree in lush green grass, half asleep. A beautiful young woman, dressed in a flowing white dress, came to him. She had raven black hair and beautiful almond shaped eyes - different eyes than he had ever seen. It was not a thinking dream, but a feeling dream. All he really knew was that he was in love with her. The message that he got from her telepathically was, "I am here ... for you. And you are here for me."

Oddly, the first question his dad had asked him was about the kind of eyes she had. He proceeded to tell Jack that when he was in China during the war, the most beautiful women he had ever seen were Asian. Growing up on a farm, Jack had never actually seen an Asian. He started asking his dad about these strange feelings he was having (pointing to his loin area), and his dad masked his nervousness by laughing it off and telling him a sex joke.

Ten years later, Jack would write about this dream in an essay for an English class. With the dream still vivid in his mind he wrote, "She had the wisdom of a grandmother, the nurturing of a mother, the beauty of a lover, and the innocence of a child."

Then there was the time Jack tried to explain a spiritual experience he had. His father told him a pope joke.

The fact was, when Frank was a young father, he would get beside himself about intimate things. He could be really mushy and cute with babies, but would act macho almost all other times. When they lived on the farm, Jack had a wonderful dog named Blackie, a collie and shepherd mix. Jack's dad was always cursing at, and complaining about "the goddam dog". But one night, Jack had walked quietly out to the barn and found his Dad talking sweet to the dog. He was scratching the dog's neck and saying, "Good dog Blackie. Yes, you are a good ole dog." That was the beginning of Jack's realization that his father had more heart than he let on.

When Jack's parents had moved from their farm in Laceyville, Pa., to the city of Wilkes-Barre, Pa., Blackie stayed on his grandparent's farm. Jack would accompany his father to the farm to help with some of the farm work on weekends. One weekend in particular, Jack's father and two uncles were discussing a growth on Blackie's hind end. It was prostate cancer. They didn't know what to do with him. Jack's father finally blurted out, "Well, hell. You can't leave the goddam dog suffer. Give me a rifle. I'll have to go up over the hill and shoot him, since neither of you seem to have the balls to do it."

Jack was old enough to know it had to be done, and he tried to hold back his tears. Blackie had been Jack's childhood companion. He said his goodbyes to Blackie as the dog licked his face one last time. Then Jack's dad walked up over the hill with the dog. A long time passed, and everyone kept looking toward the hill, waiting to hear the gunshot. The gunshot never came, but Jack's dad came back over the hilltop wiping his eyes, with Blackie frolicking behind him. Everyone let out a nervous relieved laugh, and one of Jack's uncles mimicked, "What's the matter? No balls?"

Jack's dad handed the uncle $10, and said in a low voice, "Here, have the vet put him to sleep and don't give me no shit. Bury him up there on the hill, and I'll carve up one of those quarry stones for him."

Then there was the time Jack had graduated from computer school, and his father was there to take him to apply for a job. They passed by IPM in Norweg, and his dad told him to go in and apply. "No," said Jack, "They would never hire me. I don't have a degree. You don't understand, Dad. That is **THE** IPM. They are not going to hire **me**!"

His father said, "Well it wouldn't hurt to put in an application now, would it? Godammit."

At the time, Jack thought his father was just being ignorant and reluctantly went in to apply only to pacify him. To Jack it seemed a waste of time. IPM kept him there taking tests, and he was sure he didn't do well on them. As it turned out, IPM was desperate for computer operators, and Jack was hired. From his father, Jack learned that anything was possible.

Jack vowed to himself that he would always be there for his children. If he had a son, he would want him to remember him as he was beginning to remember his father. Fondly. Warmly. Proudly.

The rest of the trip to their large Yuppie suburban townhouse in Newtown was the usual. Lynn reviewed the whole funeral again, including all the faux pas Jack had made. Evidently, he hadn't talked to Aunt Marion enough and he had actually laughed so loud with his sister that everyone could hear them. My God, people would think he didn't care. And to top it all off, he had also left Lynn alone to go talk to his relatives. And what was that going on when he rode in the limo behind the hearse with his sister? It looked like they were laughing and having a big party, she said. Jack's whole family had no clue. Do you people really care?

Jack had hoped that she would come through and show him a little compassion that day. He wanted badly to feel more intimate with her. She had so much potential, and they could love each other so much, if she would let him get close to her.

But, she never once held his hand or touched him. He felt so alone in the world. It was a long ride home. When he pulled into the driveway, he breathed a sigh of relief. He knew he could finally be by himself and think in peace.

After he arrived home he wrote his feelings down in a poem.

The Failure

Lonely days
And lonely nights.
Sadness, tears,
And silly fights.

More and more
I realize.
There is no end,
No compromise.

There is no more
That I can do,
Even though
I feel for you.

There is no more
That I can say.
I've tried and failed
Too many a day.

That night, Jack sat on the couch feeling deeply sad about the loss of his father. Lynn came in the room and misread his silence. "You are so unemotional. So stoic." she criticized.

He looked down and replied, "I do have feelings." He suddenly felt the need to tell her exactly what was on his mind. "It's just that you <u>still</u> don't know me after all these years. You can't even see how much I'm hurting. You interpret the things I do as if I were someone else. And you attribute the things I do to lesser motives. And you know what?! I don't **LIKE** the person that you think I am."

She rolled her eyes, and said, "There you go talking in circles, Jack." She had a frigid way of saying "Jack".

Jack retorted, "You know, sometimes I feel like BECOMING that person you think I am, just to see how you would react."

"Well Jaack," she said smugly, "Then you could do what you really want to do. You could go out and get drunk with the boys. You could start slapping me around. You could start whoring around. I know that's what you really want to do. But I'll tell you, Jaack, if you start doing any of that, I'm gone, and I'll take you for everything you have. Do you hear me, Jack? Hit me once, just once, I dare you."

"I've never hit a woman," he replied in a calmer, more definite manner, "I don't enjoy going out for the sake of getting drunk with the boys, and I don't whore around."

She shook her head. "Yeah? You men are all alike. I know you, Jack. Don't lie to me."

Jack just looked straight ahead. He took a breath and said something that he knew she was going to misunderstand, but he had to try one more time. Maybe the right words would come out this time. "I am not like your father," he said.

She attacked immediately. "Don't you dare insinuate those things about my father! Do I talk about **your** father?"

"As a matter of fact, you do," he said.

"Well, hah!" she said redeemingly, "Your father is no comparison to mine. My father didn't **leave** his family. He provided for us very well. Thanks to **your** father, you were piss-poor, and then he left you for his whore."

Jack tried to explain himself. "I didn't mean to say anything negative about your father. I just want you to understand <u>me</u>."

She smirked, "I understand you perfectly well, Jack. If it weren't for me, you would be married to some low class bitch. Maybe she would help you with all your properties. Maybe she could clean them for you. She might even help you carry things. Is that what you want? You want some farm girl that will ride with you in your pick-up truck? Well, that isn't me

Jack." Suddenly, she changed her tune in midstream, as if she were changing the station on the radio. She said seductively, "Come on, let's stop this foolishness and go to bed."

Jack looked at her, amazed, and answered, "I don't feel like going to bed. I'm too upset."

She moved closer sliding her hand up and down his thigh and mocked condescendingly, "Oh come on, Jack. Let's go upstairs."

"NO."

She paused and looked at him. She changed her tune again, this time feigning concern. "You know, Jack. I'm worried about you. You haven't been interested in sex lately. Can I ask you something without you getting all upset?"

"Go ahead," he answered, resigned.

"Are you questioning your sexuality? Be honest. Are you a ... a ... homosexual?"

Jack looked at her with pained awe. He could not believe that she could question him that way after the fifteen years they had spent together. Their sexual relations had always been good. How could she think that of him?

She saw his pained face and misinterpreted it. "You are, aren't you, Jack? Come on. You can tell me."

Jack felt a cloud of hopelessness enveloping him. He looked at her intensely and said, "You don't know me at all."

She responded arrogantly, "What is there to know? You lie to me about your feelings."

"I don't lie," he said. "It's just that when I tell you how I really feel, it doesn't fit your perception of me and, since you always have to be right, you don't believe me, and I never get heard. All these years, you have not been married to **ME**. You have been married to your own skewed perception of me."

She responded melodiously and sarcastically, "Oh Please! You are talking in circles again. Are you trying to tell me I'm crazy?"

Jack finally lost it and yelled, "No! **I'M** the one who's crazy and getting crazier by the day! I **have** to leave you. I can't stand the loneliness, anymore."

She said arrogantly, "Loneliness? Look Jack. I offered for you to go upstairs with me, and now you are telling me you are lonely. I asked you if you think I'm crazy, and you say you're the crazy one. Maybe you need to take some more of those psychology courses and figure yourself out. In the meantime, if you want a little nookie, come upstairs." She mocked, "Poor Jackie. Nobody understands him." She sashayed up the stairs. "Stay down there and feel sorry for yourself then."

Jack felt relieved that she was gone. He needed to grieve for his father's death, but his wife kept entering his thoughts. He always doubted himself so much after talking to her. Maybe he **was** stoic and unemotional. Maybe she was just trying to help him by releasing his feelings. No. That wasn't something she would do. What if she were right? If he hadn't married her, would he have become a drunk? No. Actually, he had stopped **her** from drinking. He found her drunk twice when she was pregnant and he had **demanded** her not to drink. It was out of character for Jack to make demands or give ultimatums in a relationship, but that time he felt he had to. In the few times he had been demanding in their marriage, she had actually responded favorably and appeared to like it. Her father was demanding and Jack knew she saw it as a sign of strength. But he couldn't dominate someone that way. He didn't want that type of relationship.

She ended up getting an abortion, saying that she just couldn't stand to be pregnant "right now" and "maybe later". It made her sick, and she couldn't stand the thought of having stretch marks. Jack was devastated. He loved kids.

Lynn had never really tried to understand his feelings. All she wanted to do was to be the princess and have Jack cater to **her** feelings. His function was to make her happy and when he didn't, he paid dearly. She was a first degree black belt put-down artist. She could push all his buttons and send him into overload in a very short period of time. She was actually a milder version of her father, who made his fortune through the manipulation and control of others. It's no wonder Lynn had been his favorite child. He had certainly taught her well.

She had heard Jack threaten to leave before. She didn't think he would dare. She thought she had control of him. After all, he had married above his class. She thought he didn't dare to get her too upset. She mistook his respect for her as weakness.

By the same token, Jack mistook her arrogance for confidence. He mistook her ego for self esteem, and he mistook her sense of entitlement for a sense of purpose.

After a time, Jack started thinking of his father again. Tears streamed down his face and he buried his face in a couch pillow and wept. His father's last words to him echoed in his mind, "Be happy, Jack."

Princeton

Sometime in February of 1985, Jack was having a drink with his best friend, Gale, at Winbarrys in Princeton. Winbarrys was modeled after the <u>Cheers</u> bar and was not far away from his office in Princeton. It was a place where professionals met after work for a drink, friendly conversation, and business leads. It was a gathering place for professors from the university, lawyers, elites from Princeton, and single women hopefuls. The preppie crowd. It was one block from tree-lined Main street of Princeton University.

Gale was a pretty woman with blue eyes and unruly blonde hair. Her looks would never lead you to think that she had a mouth like a sailor. This was the first time Jack had a woman as a best friend. He was very proud of that and felt he could tell Gale anything. He had no attraction for Gale sexually because when he looked at Gale, he saw his sister. So she was safe, and he was safe. Gale had been assigned to Jack at IPM to help him develop a software system.

Gale was a year older than Jack. She delighted in embarrassing him with her comments. She felt she could say anything to him without fear of being judged. It seemed to Jack that Gale could get away with saying anything to anybody. Earlier that day, when they were in a professional meeting with management. The vice president of distribution had taken Gale aside and asked her not to say "f--k" in the meetings. He said, "It's not appropriate for a lady."

Gale looked at him for a moment and replied,"OK. I'll stop saying f--k if <u>you</u> stop scratching your balls."

Jack had heard the conversation and sank down into his chair, red faced. Of course, everyone else laughed.

Gale could polish off several margaritas without missing a beat. Jack was the opposite: a conservative drinker who would order one drink and then club soda the rest of the time. The bartender knew them both and would give Jack a club soda without the straw so people would think it was a real drink. He would also add a little extra tequila to Gale's margarita.

In light of the incident with the vice president, Jack was trying to explain the limits and boundaries of certain aspects of life. "You just don't say f--k. You just don't," Jack said.

"Saying 'f--k' is no worse than scratching your balls. How would they like it if I started scratching my itchy tits?" Gale argued as she made a face and started moving her breasts around in her bra to get them in a more comfortable position and to prove her point. Several people in the bar looked over and Jack turned away from her, embarrassed again. Gale smiled triumphantly over Jack as she waved to one of the men who kept staring at her.

In all her thirty nine years, Gale had been to bed with a total of 4 men. Two of whom she had children with. So Jack knew the man who was lustfully gazing at Gale might as well not waste his time. "OK," said Gale, now with two margaritas under her belt, "See those girls over there?" she pointed.

"Yes, answered Jack, wondering what she had up her sleeve.

"Do you like the way they look?"

"Yeah. Kind of young, though."

"So, if you weren't married," asked Gale," how old would they have to be before you would hit on them?"

"25," said Jack.

"OK," Gale said slapping her hand on the bar, "I happen to know that the redhead is 24 years old. I know you are attracted to her because I've seen you look over there enough times tonight. So, would you go out with her?" The auburn haired young woman that Jack had been glancing at was in her prime. She had perfect pale skin that coordinated excellently with her slit black dress and Cleopatra style hair. There was not a blemish on her body. She stood confidently with her legs spread apart just enough that you could see a perfect leg through the slit in her dress.

Jack said,"No, I would not go out with her."

"Why?" asked Gale.

"Because a person has to have limits," he replied. "I **wouldn't** go out with her because it wouldn't be **appropriate**, just like saying 'f--k' in a meeting with IPM executives is not appropriate. Get it?"

"So," said Gale, "you'd rather go home and play with your noodle?" She looked at him innocently with those big blue eyes, taking delight in his crimson face.

"You know, Gale," he said, "I grew up with a bunch of juvenile delinquents on the wrong side of town and they said the raunchiest things, but I have **never** been so embarrassed by anyone as I am by you." She laughed joyfully, knowing that what he said was true.

"But what if it was love at first sight?" she started, again.

Jack balked, "You don't really believe in that, do you? You are 39 years old! I thought you had more savvy than that, Gale. There is no such thing. There's infatuation. There's lust. But there's no Prince who is going to come riding up on his white steed and sweep you off your feet. That's how women end up with frogs, you know. The frog dresses up like a Prince, and then one day you turn over to look at him and see the warts on his face. God, Gale! I hate it when people believe in love at first sight. That there is <u>one</u> meant just for them. I lose respect for anyone who believes that. God, I hate that! That has screwed up more lives. There is no Prince or

Princess and there is no love at first sight. Only in Hollywood. How many marriages have you seen that start out like that and as soon as the illusion wears off ... "

"My my," she interrupted coyly, "Aren't we all worked up?! You better have a Margarita. Don't you believe in true love?"

"Sure I do," he said, "But it's a process. You have to work at it. You never get something for nothing in this world. If it looks that way, there's something wrong. It's always on the buy-now pay-later plan. Save the Princess now, and cater to the frog later. I really dislike these fairy tales and movies that promote infatuation. It always wears off. All you have to do is look around to see it. It's just mother nature seducing people for the next crop of babies."

"Well, aren't we jaded," she said.

"Real," Jack quickly replied.

"Jaded!"

"Real!"

"Jaded!"

"Real!"

"JADED!"

"Bitch."

"Partypooper."

"Partypooper?!" Jack said with mock gratitude, "Gale, did you say partypooper? That's the nicest thing you have ever called me! That's really mild compared to 'dick', 'asshole,' or 'jerk'! OK. I'll have that margarita now."

They saw a young man approach the redhead sheepishly. Red looked at him and said condescendingly, "Oh God. What are **you** doing here?"

The young man looked at her longingly and said, "I want you back with me."

She replied, "Look Charlie. We have been over this. I don't want to be with you."

As he took her hand he said, "Just come outside and talk."

She pulled away and said, "No Charlie, there's nothing else to say. You are spoiling my fun here. Go away."

He took her hand again. "Pleeeze," he begged. He gripped

her hand tightly and started pulling her out.

"Bartender!" she cried, "This guy is bothering me!" The bartender, a lineman for Princeton, told Charlie that he better let her go or he would throw him out. The young man put his head down and walked out, defeated.

At the same time Gale was saying, "Bitch!" Jack was saying, "Jerk!." They looked at each other surprised.

"What do you mean ... 'Jerk'?" said Gale, "She could have at least talked to him. The poor guy loves her."

Jack objected, "He may love her, but what I saw was **obsession**."

"Well, Dr. Callahan, when you love someone, you are obsessed with them."

He replied, "No way! It's just another stupid illusion. Love is **not** obsession. Love is **not** jealousy. Love is not even **passion**. And love is certainly not any of the illusions **we** give it."

"OK smartass," Gale retorted, "You've got my attention. But when I'm in love, I am obsessed, jealous, and passionate. So you tell me, oh mighty psych-major, what is love?"

Jack stammered, "Well, its nothing I can put into words. It is beyond words, and it isn't really an 'it' at all. I had this experience once where I saw what love really is, and I can't explain ..."

Gale smirked, "So what was it? LSD? Cocaine? A good lay? How did you know ..."

"I've never done drugs, and getting laid is not it. I don't know why I had the experience that I did. Maybe it was because I was ready at that particular moment. You don't have to be a saint to have the experience; otherwise it would have never happened to me. It was just that everything that was **not** love was cleared away for a time and I was able to experience love in its purest form."

Gale looked at him, intrigued but wary. She smiled. "Who was she, Jack? It must have been great sex!"

A little annoyed, he said, "Gale, I'm trying to explain it. It wasn't <u>with</u> anybody."

She giggled heartily. "Playing with the ole noodle you had this spiritual experience?"

"All right Gale, that's it. It's not about that. It's not about being **in** love. It's not about illusions, delusions, sex, drugs, or noodles."

"God, Callahan," she said, "You're so deep now that **I'm** drowning. Have a couple margaritas. Lighten up. That redhead has been looking over at you, so I'll just go over and convince her that she needs to have a spiritual experience with you, OK? I really think that once you get drunk and get laid, you'll forget all this deep shit. Hell, you're killing all my illusions. No prince. No obsessions. No passion. No sex. What the f--k is there to look forward to? No meaning in life.."

"Love ...," said Jack, warmly and confidently, "<u>is</u> meaning in and of itself."

"All right Jack, I'll contemplate what you said tomorrow, when I'm sober. But for now, I am going to settle for another margarita and look for some rich guy who wants a 39 year old blonde sex goddess from Brooklyn with two kids, her own house in the suburbs, and the best sex he has ever had."

A few margaritas later, Gale looked at Jack intensely. He looked back. "What, Gale? I can hear you thinking so loud, my ears are ringing." She looked at him lovingly.

"You know Jack. I care for you a lot."

Jack said, "Say you care for me a BUNCH, Gale."

She looked at him funny. "OK. I care for you a bunsch."

"You're drunk, Gale."

"Jack, you sonufabitch. Nevermind that," she said, regrouping as she put her hand on his shoulder, "I'm your friend. Your best friend. So Jack. I'm going to step over my limits, as you would say, and tell you something."

He laughed, "**You** have **limits?!**"

"Not that I like to admit," she smiled coyly, regaining her composure. "But I'm drunk enough to tell you what your problem is. I mean, I've never tried to interfere with someone's marriage because marriage is sacred, you know.

But your marriage is ... evil." She looked quickly for his reaction through squinted eyes.

"Evil! Hell," mocked Jack, "If you have something to say, just say it, Gale. I mean, don't beat around the bush. Get right to the point."

Gale began again. "I'm serious. I've been around you and your wife. And I have nothing to gain from saying this. I don't want your body, or your job, or your money. But I really can't believe the things your wife says to you without really saying them. And you believe these things ... you're such a good-hearted wimp ... you're critical of yourself to the exact degree that she exaggerates your faults. She controls you with your low opinion of yourself and your self doubt. She is inside your mind rewarding you for fulfilling her wishes and punishing you when you go off the straight and narrow. You are her 'boy'. And I'm here to tell you that you are better than that. She doesn't know you and she doesn't care to know you, except to know what your buttons are. And she does know **all** your buttons. She's like a crocodile floating in the water with a big smile. She won't eat you if she's not hungry. But if she gets hunger pains she will have you for dinner. Pretty good insight for someone who's drunk, huh!?" She leaned back to study him.

"OK, smart lady," he said jokingly, yet seriously, "You spotted the problem, so what's the solution?"

Gale started singing an old song, "Just slip out the back, Jack. Get a new plan, Stan. You don't need to be coy, Roy. Just listen to me."

"And then what?" Jack asked.

"Well then," she said with feigned excitement, "You come back to Winbarrys, have a few margaritas, and screw that redhead who has been looking at your crotch all night."

He glanced over at the redhead who smiled and looked away. Jack looked away too quickly. Then, Gale, having seen that, said, "You are such a pussy-footer, Callahan."

He was unsure if he should be offended. "What's a pussy-footer?" he asked.

Gale acted like a cat walking with her hands. Her voice whispered, "You know. Like you walk softly, so you don't offend anyone or hurt their feelings. Pussy-footer. You do it at work. You do it at home. You even do it with me."

Jack suddenly got a mischievous smile on his face and GROWLED like a lion right in Gale's face. He had caught her off guard, and she fell off the bar stool right onto the floor.

He was immediately embarrassed for her. He didn't expect her to be that surprised. He began apologizing as Gale howled with laughter. A man who had been staring at Gale came over to help Jack pick her up. He offered to drive her home.

She acted interested in him as she came off the floor and said, "Look. I have six kids at home, and I want to get married to a guy who will love my children and who has a 6 inch tongue and can breathe through his ears 'cause I like oral sex. Are you my soulmate? Hey, I really hope you're here to save my ass. It's a nice ass, really, for having six kids."

The man smiled and went back to his seat. Gale turned to Jack and sighed, "Well, I guess that wasn't him."

Jack said, "Why did you lie to that guy? You don't have six kids."

"Aw c'mon Jack. It's all in fun. You know, people in a bar will believe anything you say. You can rattle off any kind of statistic, and they believe it. You can tell them you're a millionaire and they'll believe it. Alcohol is a hypnotic. It makes people suggestible. Try it sometime. It's fun to deliberately lie, just to see someone's reaction. Lying isn't wrong unless someone gets hurt. Besides, that guy just wanted to f--k my brains out and go home to his wife by three AM."

"Gale," he said admiringly, "you are sanely crazy sometimes."

Jack drove Gale home to her house just outside Princeton and hugged her before she staggered up the driveway to her large expensive home.

Yes, he was a pussy-footer. He had come to recognize

patterns in his life. It seems that people didn't appreciate him until he was gone. At work, he could spot potential disasters and nip them in the bud. His bosses had always attributed his success to "luck" and would pass him over for promotions. Then after Jack would take another job, they would realize how much he contributed to the job and the morale and want him back ... with the promotion. Jack could take a lot of stress, and in fact, worked rather well under stress. He had managed to pay his way through college while working for IPM. He had his bachelor's degree in Computer Science and Master's degree in Psychology. He had married at age 23. Lynn had been pregnant. He had decided to <u>make</u> the marriage work, and he <u>had</u>.

Jack appeared to be so easy going that people were always surprised when he stood up for himself, or for something he believed in. If an issue was important to him, he just wouldn't back down.

He saw himself as someone who lacked personality. His wife reinforced this belief over and over. He felt it took a long time for people to know him. It did. But once people knew him, they trusted him and liked him. He wasn't inclined to say anything bad about another, even when it was true. People often mistook his kindness for weakness, and his lack of egotism for lack of confidence.

Jack had an utmost respect for women, and his wife used this to her advantage. She also used his white-knight mentality to bail her out of situations (like bouncing checks). She could also feign sickness or tiredness, and Jack would swing into action to help.

However, Jack had never been happy in his marriage, and he felt solely responsible for his unhappiness, thinking that perhaps he was too immature to handle marriage. His wife agreed, of course. He would always try to change things in himself. But for everything he changed, his wife had two other complaints. One of the reasons he had studied psychology was to figure out what his problem was. He had also gone for therapy himself. His wife participated very little in his therapy because she felt it was Jack who had the problem. "Jack was not mature enough. He came from a poor family background. He was not responsible enough. He had no idea how to treat a wife. He was always laughing like a little kid. Grow up, Jack! Get serious." She would compare him to one of her old boyfriends, Tim Robbins. "Tim had class. He knew how to treat a lady. He had a personality. He had a mature laugh. He was older and wiser. I wish you were a little older, Jack." If Jack could be more like him, then maybe she would be happy. "I am not happy because of <u>you</u>, Jack. If you would only support me in the way I am accustomed to. I am not used to <u>budgeting</u>." If only Jack had a little more class ... if he was more mature ... if he made a little more money ... maybe ... she would be happy ... and then maybe ... she would love him. Great sex though, Jack!

A song would play on the car radio, and he would catch her staring longingly with a tear in her eye. He knew she was thinking of Tim Robbins, but she would never admit it. He would try harder. Buy flowers. Scratch her back more often. Try to be more understanding. Get those promotions and raises. Make more money. But he could never seem to measure up to her expectations.

Jack worked hard at improving himself. He had tried to find out what love really was. He read every good self-help book on the market and every book on love that he could find. What he realized was that love is not an idea. Love is not a perspective or a way of thinking. It's not about all that and cannot be perceived with thought. It's not a feeling (although there is a <u>feeling</u> of love). It's not infatuation or lust. It doesn't die or end. It isn't sex. Yet he couldn't feel love coming from Lynn. It seemed to be elusive.

He couldn't understand where he was going wrong.

Before he got Lynn pregnant, he thought he would go to China and bring back a beautiful Chinese girl. His puerile fantasy was that he would save her from the depths of poverty, and maybe that would be enough to make up for his lack of personality. Then, they would live happily ever after.

He felt he had to have an edge. No one would accept him just for himself. He needed accomplishments, money, and status. But that fantasy was over. He had married someone for whom he could never be good enough.

The next day, Jack went to see his therapist. He was able to get an appointment over his lunch hour. Dr. Mintz was a psychologist who had been Jack's mentor through his master's degree in psychology. Jack felt he could confide in him. Dr. Mintz was about the same age as Jack. He was a Jewish guy from New York City, with a mischievous smile, lots of curly black hair, and a beard. Mintz didn't beat around the bush about anything. When Jack first met with him, he didn't like Mintz. Mintz was confrontational and Jack thought he was a cocky arrogant New Yorker. Then Mintz had said to Jack, "You know. I am cocky and arrogant. Do you think we can work together?" After that, Jack liked him. Sometimes he seemed to able to read Jack's mind.

Dr. Mintz motioned Jack into his office. Jack sat down as the doctor lit his pipe. "Good to see you again, Jack. What's going on?"

Jack started, "Well, I can't stay in my marriage, but if I leave, Lynn will turn everyone against me, and I couldn't stand that. Also, her family is going to think I am a low-life, just as they suspected. And my friends may think I am a bastard, except maybe for my friend, Gale."

"What does Gale say?" asked Mintz.

"She says I am a pussyfooter. That's someone who ... "

"I know what it means, Jack," interrupted Mintz, "You don't want people to think you are a bastard. You don't want your wife to think it, or your friends, or your boss, or even me."

"Of course not!" said Jack, "I'm not a bastard."

Mintz leaned forward and said, "And, it would just kill you to have people think you were a bastard."

"Yes," said Jack, "because I work very hard to maintain my relationships."

"Why?" Mintz asked.

"What do you mean, 'Why'?" retorted Jack. "Hell, if people didn't give a damn about relationships, the whole world would be in chaos!"

"No Jack," Mintz replied. "I understand that. But, I think one of the reasons why <u>you</u> work so hard at relationships is that you want everyone to like you. You sell out. You see, you are not <u>willing</u> to be a bastard. Not that you <u>are</u> a bastard. But you are not <u>willing</u> to have others <u>think</u> you are a bastard, so you sell out." Mintz drew on his pipe and blew a smoke ring.

"Hmmmm," Jack thought out loud. "Can you explain a little more?"

"Do you remember our first meeting?" asked Mintz.

"Yes," answered Jack.

"I told you I was a cocky and arrogant. You see, I am willing to be a bastard. It's therapeutic sometimes. <u>You</u> don't have that option. You pussyfoot around so people will like you. You sell out."

"Aha!" realized Jack. "That's why people feel they can take advantage of me. That's why people lose respect for me. That's why sometimes I don't have respect for myself ... because I change myself so that the other person likes me ... then I am no longer myself ... and if that person likes me then ... they are really liking someone else, not really me! So, as long as I am not willing to be a bastard in someone else's eyes, I'm stuck."

Dr. Mintz responded, "That's an excellent intellectual insight, Jack. You are very bright. Can you excuse me for a minute? I have to use the bathroom."

"Sure," said Jack.

Dr. Mintz got up and left for ten minutes. When he returned, he had a pitcher of water in his hand. He nodded to Jack, "Keep talking, Jack. I'm listening. I just have to water these plants in my office before I forget. They need water badly."

Jack looked a little annoyed as Dr. Mintz turned his back to water the plants, but he tried to say something anyway.

"So," Jack added hesitantly, "maybe I should be more demanding, even if people don't like me, for my own self respect."

Dr. Mintz was clearly not paying much attention. Now he was pulling the dead leaves off his plants.

"Yes. Go on, Jack. I'm listening."

Jack was uneasy. "So to leave my marriage, I have to be willing to be a bastard ... knowing that some people will actually think I am."

"Yes, Jack," said Mintz as he suddenly whirled around. "Hey, look. I apologize, but I must have diarrhea or something. I'll be right back." He dashed out of the room and stayed out for fifteen minutes this time!! Jack was left looking at his watch, wondering if he was going to be charged for the whole session, wondering if Dr. Mintz was getting tired of him or bored with him.

When Dr. Mintz came back, he was looking at his watch and said, "Jack, look, you only have five minutes left. Do you mind if we end early? I have to meet my wife for lunch."

Normally Jack wouldn't have minded, but Mintz had already taken too much time from the session. So Jack said, "You aren't going to charge me for the full session, are you?"

Dr. Mintz looked at him, puzzled. "Well, of course. You were here the whole time."

Jack started boiling. "Yes, but you weren't," he said.

"Hey, Jaack," Mintz said in his Long Island New York accent, "I'm human. I've got bodily functions too, you know."

Jack finally snapped. "Yes, but you spent 25 minutes taking a crap!"

Mintz shook his head and looked at Jack. "After all I've done for you, you are going to be 'anal' about this?"

"You have done a lot for me," said Jack, "And, I don't want to piss you off , but ..."

Mintz interrupted. "Then be a good client, and don't piss me off!"

"Well," started Jack vehemently, "if I have to sit there while you water your plants, weed your plants, and take a crap, then

I'm not getting what I paid for. And, if I'm not getting anything out of this, then why should I come here?!"

"EXACTLY," said the smiling Mintz.

Jack paused. He looked at that mischievous smile and finally caught on. Then he began laughing uncontrollably. In the midst of his laughter, he said, "Well thanks for being such a cocky, arrogant, New Yorker."

Dr. Mintz gave him a knowing smile and said, "You're welcome, Jack. And make sure you pay the secretary for the whole session ... you bastard."

Jack smiled the whole way back to work. He slipped a tape into his cassette and he started to sing along. "I can see clearly now. The rain is gone ..."

He felt free of a great burden. He felt like he could be ... had to be ... himself now. "So," he thought to himself, "that's the definition of a bastard -- someone who is not willing to do what someone else wants them to do or be what someone else wants them to be. Well, I'm not going to be what Lynn wants me to be, so I guess I'm going to be a bastard. I never thought it would feel this good to be a bastard, and to think I have waited so long to become one. My, my," he laughed to himself, "she is going to have to like me the way I am."

In the months that followed, Jack dropped all pretenses in his marriage. He told Lynn he would no longer be responsible for making her happy. Only she could make herself happy. And, she was going to have to start helping to carry the ball in their marriage.

She didn't really know how. He had enabled her for so long, that she just couldn't contribute. She resorted to her usual put-down techniques, but he wouldn't listen anymore. She had abused their communication for so long that he had become immune. She even resorted to telling him he was just like his father, but this time he thanked her for the compliment.

He told her that he didn't love her the way a man should

love his wife, that the candle had been flickering too long and had gone out for good. He told her that he had been unhappy in the marriage for a long time and wanted a separation. He moved his clothes to the recroom in the lower level and slept there at night. She tried to change her behavior. She even offered to scratch his back, but her heart wasn't in the right place, and she just had no idea how to make a husband feel good. She was used to being the princess and being catered to. She was operating on the fear of losing him rather than from the heart. She was hoping his restlessness would pass, calling it a mid-life crisis. But the marriage had died, leaving only the structure in place with no substance.

Over several months, there was no sex between them. She asked him again if he was gay, and this time she wanted the truth. He felt like saying yes, just to hurt her. She told family and friends that she thought he was having an affair. Two of her friends later came on to him. He felt like having sex with them, just to hurt her and to create an incident so she would leave him, but he maintained his integrity. Then, he hoped she would have an affair, so he could blame her and look like the good guy. But he thought that would be too devious, and he would be ashamed of himself. At one point, he thought she might be seeing someone. He had awakened at four in the morning to hear her car drive into the driveway. When he looked for some sort of jealousy inside himself, he could find none. He actually wouldn't blame her if she did have an affair.

Jack went off to work everyday as usual. One day, Jack's boss, Ed, asked him to travel to Manila in the Philippines to set up a software system. "You'll only be gone for two weeks. Can you go?"

The timing was good, Jack thought. He needed to be alone to think. It would also relieve the daily tension of living with

Jay Carter

Lynn.
 "I'll go," he said.

On May 16, 1985, Jack was at the Holiday Inn near Makati, Manila, in the Philippines. He was glad to be on the other side of the earth, as far away as he could get from his unhappy marriage of fifteen years. His work assignment in the Philippines was finished and he was touristing.

Even though Jack had separated from his wife, he was still living in the same house. There had been two floors between them for the past six months, and their communication had been cordial but distant. For him, the marriage was over, and he had told his wife he would be seeking a divorce. The candle inside him that he had kept flickering for a long time had finally gone out. Now there were the decisions about what to **do**. Jack had felt lonely for fifteen years. Jack felt like he had tried everything to remedy the marriage for fifteen years and failed. The stubborn part of himself was finally ready to throw in the towel and stop trying to make it go right.

So there he was, puffing on a cigar in the middle of Manila, contemplating what he should do. This was not a new contemplation. However, Jack really needed to make a decision this time. The man-woman love Jack had for his wife was gone and he would never get it back. Jack wasn't even attracted to her physically anymore, although she was an attractive woman. The last time they had sex was over six months before Jack had moved to the recroom on the bottom floor. Once, Jack had aroused her in his sleep, and when he awoke, he was in the middle of things and so was she. When Jack realized what was happening, he could only think to himself, "Oh no!" It seemed so hypocritical, but he faked it through to the end and when it was over, he was thoroughly disgusted with himself. He knew then he couldn't continue his marriage with Lynn, even for her sake. She was young and attractive enough to find someone else, and if he stayed he would be doing her an injustice.

His original plan had been to give it one more year, but

Jack could not do that. He could feel himself on the verge of getting some sort of stress related illness. He was experiencing chest pain and the beginnings of an ulcer. If something happened to him, what good would he be? No, he had to make a decision **today** at the Holiday Inn in Manila.

An executive told Jack once, "Sometimes it doesn't matter what decision you make as much as long as you **make** a decision." That day Jack decided three things: He was going to pursue the career he had always wanted; Work came second; and he did not need a woman in his life. "What the hell," he thought, "I have been lonely for fifteen years. What is a few more?" Jack would buy a house and move out. Jack already owned several houses that he had renovated and now managed, so the financial stress factor would be small. He had accumulated enough real estate and equity that the financial problems would not come from a lack of money, just maybe the logistics. He was already resigned to the fact that his wife would get half of everything, and he would not be fighting about that with her.

After making these decisions, Jack felt renewed. For the first time, he realized that he did not **need** a woman in his life to be happy. As a matter of fact, he was glad not to have a woman in his life in the "mate" category. He breathed a cleansing sigh of relief.

Jack thought about his best friend, Gale. It was nice having a woman for a best friend. Gale was a real character. Jack could tell her anything. He could depend on her. She was a woman who cared for him.

The sexual side to his life? He would have to deal with that as it came. Jack was never one for one-night stands. He had tried it a couple times and the empty feeling the next day wasn't worth it.

He flashed back to an affair he had at one of the lowest ebbs in his marriage. He liked Kelly from the start and was very attracted to her and she to him. She kept "getting in his face", touching him, and generally letting him know she wanted him. But clueless Jack did not respond. That just made the challenge all the more for Kelly, and she was going to keep trying until he responded one way or the other. One day, she was feeling her oats and went nose to nose with him. She had that kind of Barbra Streisand personality. Jack's face was crimson, as he revealed his ethical dilemma to Kelly. "Kelly," he sighed, "I am very attracted to you. I like you, I care for you, and I wouldn't want anyone I cared for having an affair with a married man. It never works out. First I would scratch your back, then you would scratch mine, then we end up in bed. One of us, or both, falls in love and gets hurt. I am not going to leave my marriage and I am not going to hurt anyone."

"Oh Jack," she patronized, "look. I'm a big girl. I like you too and I want your body. I lived with a guy for two years and I have decided that I don't want a man around all the time. I'll probably never get married. So what does that leave me? An unhappily married man like yourself. I control who I fall in love with, and I expect that you also control that. So, Jack ... let's skip the back scratching and go right to the bedroom. I've wanted you for a long time."

She had been holding his hands and looking straight into his eyes as she talked. Jack couldn't believe she was actually attracted to him. She actually liked him. He felt guilty but he needed her.

It was based upon liking and lusting. It was safe and they really did care for each other, along with the unbridled lust. Right or wrong, the affair saved his marriage for a few more years. Jack was sure that he had overlooked something and that this affair was probably not going to be beneficial, but he was wrong. As he looked back on it, it was an exception to the norm. It really did save his marriage.

Jack had seen Kelly since and she said she had no regrets and would have done it over again. Jack always knew that God did not play by man's rules, and he hoped that God would forgive him with His loving intent and purpose. Jack hoped God could overlook that one, given the circumstances he had gotten himself into.

Jack met Kelly again later in life, on an elevator. They made a lunch date. They had a good time talking and laughing. The pool of lust in the past had completely dried up, but the friendship remained. It's a funny thing about lust. There doesn't seem to be an end to it at the moment it is being consumed, but it does end. It's not as meaningful, but momentarily satisfying when real love is elusive. As Jack sat across the lunch table from Kelly he wasn't thinking of the lust, but the familiar fondness and love he had for her ... this time without the sexual stirrings. It wasn't a husband-wife kind of love, but it was warm and good. She was in love with someone she worked with, and Jack was happy for her.

Jack's reminiscing was interrupted by Elizabeth Labus knocking on his door. Jack had helped Elizabeth through school in the Philippines since she was 16 and she had turned into a fine young lady. Jack had set up a fund for gifted children in the Philippines and Elizabeth had been the best candidate. She had also been his guide and interpreter on other trips to the Philippines. She was a good Christian Filipino girl of good moral character and worth every bit of help Jack had given her. Like a big brother, he was proud of her accomplishments. Jack had paid her tuition to the finest school in Cebu. The tuition was 2500 pisos a year which had translated in 1980 to about $250.00. She had no idea how easy it was for him to help her, and she thought that Jack was surely a rich man. Jack tried to explain to her how trivial it was for him to help her (in terms of dollars), but she was so grateful and dedicated to him. Evidently she thought Jack was doing the standard Asian thing of minimizing his great effort, so he gave up and let her think that. How Jack loved the Philippines! And how the Philippines loved him! Jack needed to be loved. There was a distinct lack of love in his life.

But today, Jack had **made a decision**. His life was renewed with purpose and goals. He grabbed the newspaper and took Elizabeth to lunch. He felt like a heavy burden was off his shoulders.

At lunch he noticed an article about the Dumagat tribe. It showed some natives burning a tree root and it talked about how an extract from this root would "take hunger away for the day", so the Dumagats kept it on hand for those days that they could not get food. Jack showed the article to Elizabeth. She said that she had studied the Dumagats in school and knew about their culture. She said the tribe was located about two hours by car outside of Manila.

Then it hit him. What if he brought back an organic substance to the USA that could take hunger away for a whole day? What if it could be sold in health food stores and what if it actually worked!? With the right marketing, He'd be rich! Jack was ecstatic! But more than that, he was happy that he felt happy and adventurous again, after so many years.

Jack leaned across the table smiled and said to his conservative guide and friend, "Elizabeth. Would you like to go on an adventure?"

"Yes," she said, "If you want to."

Jack said, "OK. Let's go visit the Dumagats."

"Oh no," she said, "That would be too dangerous. They are not as civilized as Filipinos. They are not Christian. It is too far. We could get lost. They live in the jungle."

Jack leaned over a little farther across the table and appealing to her sense of obligation, he said purposefully, "I **want** to go." She looked at him, probably wondering what kind of an impractical, crazy American he was. She looked at him, trying to find some sense of logic or reason for him to want to do this foolish thing. Then she finally gave up and said. "OK. I'll make arrangements."

The next day, Elizabeth knocked on his door at sun-up. She found a driver that she could trust for $20.00 for the day (400 Pisos). The driver had a taxicab. They jumped into the cab and took off. The driver had brought a friend with him who knew the Dumagat area and whose family resided next to the jungle where the Dumagats lived. They were going to drive to this friend's village and then they would have to walk about 45 minutes into the jungle.

The conversation was lively, and Elizabeth interpreted Tagalog to English until Jack convinced the driver and his friend that this would be a good opportunity for them to learn to speak English. Most Filipinos understand English, but do not speak it. They watch our TV shows and read our books, but they speak their own Cebuian language in Cebu (Tagalog in Manila). After they had ridden an hour or so, Jack could understand most of what they said. It was an adventure for them too, and they were all excited.

They finally came to a stop at a creek. The road seemed to end right there. Everyone got out of the Toyota economy taxicab, and Jack asked the driver what they would do now. The driver pointed across the creek and said, "We go there." Then Jack saw it; the road continued on the other side. Little known to Jack, in the Philippines back country, bridges are scarce. The driver was assessing the best way to get the cab across the stream. Soon a jeep pulled up on the other side and a smiling Filipino got out and said a few words to the driver. Elizabeth said he was telling their driver that he would never get the cab across the water and that he would pull him with the Jeep for 4 pisos. The driver seemed offended by this and motioned for the Jeep to go away. By this time, the driver had waded into the water and was waist deep. Jack told Elizabeth to tell the driver that he would pay the 4 pisos. (About 40 cents). The driver said it was too much and he told Elizabeth that he didn't want Jack to think he was taking advantage of him by trying to get more money, so he would not ask for any. They all climbed into the car and tried to drive across the stream. Soon the water was up to the bottom of the door and the car was sliding around on the smooth rocks at the bottom of the stream. They got about halfway across and then ... they started floating down the stream. The car continued to spin its wheels in the water as they sank deeper and deeper and then finally lodged on a large rock. The driver got out of the car and uttered a few Filipino swear words while the man with the jeep stood laughing on the bank. The driver waded over to the jeep and told him he would pay for a tow. The man with the Jeep held out his hand and cheerfully said, "**Twenty** Pisos!" At that, the driver lost his cool and started throwing creek rocks at the jeep man who took shelter in the trees, laughing all the way.

The humiliated driver told Jack he was going to leave the car in the creek and they would walk the rest of the way. It was only ten miles to the village. Jack tried to tell Elizabeth to give the Jeep man twenty pisos, but she stopped him. It would only humiliate the driver more. She told him that it is most important to "save face".

Jack didn't think a ten mile walk in the hot sun was going to do his lily white skin much good, so he suggested that they try to push the car by hand. The driver was a typical 5'0" 100 lb. Filipino, and so was his friend. They looked at Jack's strapping 180 pound physique and decided to try it. Jack backed himself up against the trunk and pulled up on the bumper to lift the back of the car, and they were soon across the stream. As they flew by the Jeep man, the driver and his friend gave the finger to him, and all Jack heard for the next three miles was how "macho" he was intermixed with other endearing Tagalog words. As he sat there in his wet pants and new wet Nikey sneakers, Jack smiled and thought, "God, I love the Philippines!"

Jack felt alive and real for the first time in a long time. He felt almost like he did when he was twenty years old except that, at his age, he felt <u>lucky</u> instead of <u>invincible</u>.

In a short time they arrived at a village. The driver's friend introduced Jack to his family and they made lunch for the unlikely party of four. The village was way out in the country, and most people there had never actually seen a Caucasian except on TV. Jack sat at the picnic table with the family as the whole village proceeded to walk by, one by one, trying to get a good look at him and pretending that they just happened to be out for a stroll. Jack waved and smiled so much that his shoulder ached and his face started to twitch. One of the passers-by was a Dumagat who had married one of the villagers.

Jack asked him questions through Elizabeth, who translated English into Tagalog to the man's wife, who then translated the Tagalog into Dumagat. Jack asked him if the tree root really did take hunger away for the whole day. He said yes. Jack asked him how he felt when he took the extract. He said, "Good." Jack then asked if it was a normal-good or a high-good. He said it was a normal-good. Jack was delighted.

Then Elizabeth asked the Dumagat where the tribe was. He told her they had moved farther into the jungle because Filipinos had made some homes close to their camp. They were now two hours by foot into the jungle. He said that Jack should not risk the trip today because it would be almost dark before anyone could leave and they could get lost coming back. Jack still wanted to go, and he asked the Dumagat if he could lead them in and out. He said he could, but there were giant mosquitos, and he showed the size with both his hands and described in great detail how sick Jack would get and how painful it would be.

Jack didn't need any more convincing than that. He decided to have the driver's friend get him one of the roots, gave him some money for his trouble, and told him that Elizabeth would give him more money when he delivered the root to her. Jack arranged to have Elizabeth airmail the root to him in the USA. He had his adventure, and he was satisfied.

The trip back was uneventful. The driver's friend stayed in the village and would get the root during the next week. Jack fell asleep at the beginning of the trip and woke up to the driver and Elizabeth hooting and hollering. After Jack was totally awake, he realized that the driver had just crossed the stream that had given them so much trouble before. And Jack also realized that his damp new Nikey sneakers were now wet again. Elizabeth laughed as Jack bent down to see his feet in a pool of water on the floor.

They got back to the Holiday Inn late, and Jack gave the driver the $20 for the day and a $20 tip. (400 Pisos). He adamantly refused so much money, until Jack shamed him into thinking of how it would benefit his wife and children.

He drove Elizabeth back to the house of a friend of hers in Manila.

The next morning Elizabeth came knocking on his door and looked at him warily when Jack opened it. "Don't worry," Jack said, "No adventures today." She breathed a sigh of relief and they went for breakfast. Elizabeth took him to some of the sights he had not seen in Manila, and Jack embarrassed her by continuously stopping to talk to perfect strangers. Jack wasn't interested in the sights so much as he was interested in the people. He liked to talk to the **real** people of whatever country he was in. He asked her to take him to the slums he had seen around the airport and to the orphanages in Manila. He was always greeted with the friendly respect and hospitality that Filipinos are known for.

Jack had been writing to a woman who worked as an assistant for an actress in the Philippines. Rhonda, the actress, saw one of his letters and asked about him. On the day Jack was supposed to see her assistant, Rhonda had sent the assistant to another province on an errand. Jack's hotel phone rang and it was Rhonda. She stated her name but Jack didn't know who she was. She seemed a little offended and then told him that the person who worked for her was supposed to meet him but could not make it. Jack verbalized his disappointment and with that there was silence at the other end of the phone. It gave him enough time to think, and he said, "Well, then what are **you** doing tonight?" She said, "Well, right now, I'm waiting down in the lobby of the Holiday Inn with nothing to do." Jack laughed and told her he would be right down. He thought endearingly about how hospitable Filipinos were. So, that night Jack went out with a famous Filipina movie actress. Jack had some clue that she was well-known because as they walked in Makati so many people greeted her and said hello. Makati is the ritzy area of the Philippines. This movie actress told him that all the rich people and "foreigners" live in Makati. They passed by a supermarket, a McDonalds, and they ate in a typical Chinese restaurant. Imagine. Her assistant couldn't make it, so she was covering for her. God, Jack loved these people.

Well, it turned out that Rhonda's motives were not the best. She had deliberately sent her assistant away, because she wanted Jack for herself. She had seen his picture and thought she might want to seduce him. She was a charming and lovable character. She took him to some pretty risque shows on the Manila strip. Sometime during that evening, Jack realized that he was out with a very famous person, and his ego started haunting him almost like an unwanted troublesome erection. Wow! Look at me. Jack Callahan, out with a famous actress! They ended up talking until four in the morning back at her home in Makati. When Jack was at her home, he could hear in his head all the guys from his old neighborhood. They were ghostly echos, saying, "Hey man. She wants you. Go for it. Don't come back and have to tell us you didn't get any." She was very beautiful, and Jack had been somewhat deprived sexually. But something had changed in him since his decision about not needing a woman. Jack knew he wasn't going to have a relationship with her in any case. He was leaving for Cebu the next day.

She had invited him into her bedroom, explaining that they might wake up the maid if they talked in the living room. They sat on her bed. Then they lay on her bed. She put her hand on his chest. Jack looked over and saw in her eyes who she was. She was lonely. There was something missing from her life. Something even unknown to **her**. She was like a child. She thought she needed sex. That would fulfill her, at least for the time being. "We are not going to do anything," Jack said, much to his own chagrin.

She sat back and looked at him with a bemused smile and said, "Are you a homosexual?"

"No."

She thought for a second. "Am I not attractive to you? You know, so many Filipinos would like to be where you are."

Jack leaned toward her assertively and reassuringly and said, "You are **very** attractive to me, and I may kick myself later for this, but I don't think this is what you need."

She retorted angrily as she folded her arms, and he could see the Spanish in her pose, "Who are you to tell me what I need? Only Rhonda tells Rhonda what Rhonda needs!" Jack had hit a chord.

"Well," Jack said," I guess you found out in your life that you can't depend on a man to satisfy your needs." She listened carefully, sizing him up and then smiled coyly.

"A man satisfies me only when I am on top." They both laughed.

The mood changed. She felt safe to open up to him. She told him that her father left her and her mother in Cebu and how she struggled to survive. She told him she met her father again after many years, and her father didn't seem like her father. He was so handsome. She said she had lain with him in bed because she wanted him to fill the emptiness inside. She asked Jack if she was wrong to do that, not really wanting an answer. She showed him the pictures of her shows and movies. She showed him her art. She would pause every now and again and say something like, "You're not from the National Inquirer are you?" and they would laugh.

At four in the morning, Jack couldn't stay awake anymore, so she called a cab for him. She asked for his address before he left and made him promise to write to her and be her friend. Jack hugged her and kissed her with love on the cheek. She had tears in her eyes as Jack left.

On the way home, Jack was annoyed by his very large erection. The biological beast in him was terribly unsatisfied. His ego was berating him. But his heart felt good. Jack knew he had done the right thing even as his ego was chiming in, telling him how stupid he was. The taxi cab driver said, "So, you were a guest of Rhonda's tonight, ah?"

"Yep." Jack said.

"You know," he said, "many Filipinos would like to be in your place."

Jack started to tell him he had the wrong idea, but then ended up just tiredly saying "Yes, I know."

Morning arrived just a couple of hours later. Jack awoke to a persistent knocking at his door. He opened the door and Elizabeth came walking in, all sweaty and frustrated. "I've been knocking a long time. I thought you left without me." She tried to pretend she wasn't angry.

"Do you know this actress named Rhonda?" Jack said.

"Oh," she said, "Where did you see her?"

His ego raised its ugly head and mentally banged his chest. "I was with her last night," Jack said as egotistically humble as he could. Then Elizabeth started an excited monologue telling him how famous Rhonda was and the all movies she was in.

Filipinos are usually very conservative and have strict rules about morals, but they seem to have another set of rules for their movie stars. The movie stars seem to live out the repressed fantasies of the general population, and the people reward them by accepting their behavior.

All the while Elizabeth was going on and on, his ego felt redeemed. Yep. There you were, Callahan. You and the famous actress. You could've had her, but you did the right thing. Jack was always so amazed at some of the thoughts that came out of the lower regions of his brain. Jack called them thoughts that he **had** as compared to thoughts that he **created**.

After Jack's ego was sufficiently satisfied, he started packing his things to go to Cebu, which was Elizabeth's home city. Jack had advanced her a plane ticket to meet him in Manila and it was time for her to go home. She wanted Jack to meet her relatives and he was anxious to meet them. They checked out of the hotel and took a cab to Manila airport, bound for Cebu.

On May 18, 1985, Jack was at the Buddhist Temple by the sea in Cebu, with Elizabeth Labus. The Temple was magnificent, located on the side of a mountain by the sea. It was a very large structure going up the mountain and exceeding the top. It was well maintained with nary a paint chip. It looked grand, as he was staring up from the bottom. It appeared to reach right into the blue sky. It was a long trek up the hill to the ornate and colorful temple, and then up the many steps inside to the top of the temple. All along the way were the small tan friendly Filipinos who made Jack love this country. Jack always felt so differently special in the Philippines. "Macho" was their word for strong and big and the word had no negative connotations there. It carried a different meaning than in the USA. Being of average height in the USA, Jack was a head taller than most Filipinos, making him feel very tall.

On the way to the top floor of the temple, they came upon some men unloading a cart full of large hemp rice bags. One of the old men carrying a rice bag lost his balance on the steps in front of him, and Jack was able to steady him. The old man laughed and said thank you, showing the few teeth he had in his mouth. Jack decided to stop and help him unload the rest of the cart. The rice bags were easy for him to carry, and Jack wanted to mingle with the people. (He also wanted to show off, while pretending humility, and hear the people say "Macho!"). It was the kind of experience Jack just couldn't get at home. Here, he got to know what it was like to stand out and be appreciated. When they were done, the old man offered him a drink of water and a little chat. Luckily, Jack had Elizabeth to interpret.

On the top floor of the Buddhist Temple there are altar-like tiers of burning candles. Most Filipinos are Catholic, but also come to the Buddhist temple to make requests. Elizabeth told Jack she had asked for a sponsor for her studies, and then she found **him**. She went over to one of the altars to light a candle. Meanwhile, Jack noticed a Chinese monk looking at him and smiling. Jack smiled back and looked away. Then Jack noticed in his peripheral vision that the monk was approaching him. Jack hated to have strangers approach him; it is always because they want something. Well hell, no one knew him here, so Jack could say no if he wanted to. Jack had turned and started walking the other way when the monk stopped him. "Hey! You want to throw sticks?" he said.

"No thanks," Jack muttered. Then the monk turned away, and Jack thought he was going to leave him alone. Hell, he was a monk. They are not supposed to be obnoxious. He looked like Buddha, with his stomach sticking out, and a wide grin on his chubby face.

The next thing Jack knew, the monk was standing in front of him holding a bunch of ornate looking sticks with all kinds of Chinese writing carved on them. "You throw sticks," he says, "And I tell you future."

"Ah damn," Jack thought. Without looking at him, Jack said, "How much?" Everybody wants money from the Caucasian.

"Free," he said, "Make donation if you want." Well, that's unusual here. Free.

"OK," Jack said, and threw the sticks as he had seen others do.

Scarcely looking at the sticks, the monk said seriously "Sticks say you going to meet somebody special." "Of course I'm going to meet someone special," thought Jack. That's what Jack disliked about these so-called fortune tellers. They generalize.

So Jack said arrogantly, "Yeah? **When?**" The monk was still looking at him, smiling.

"A day or two." he said. Well that's different! An actual time commitment. Wait a minute! he'd get him this time.

"Well, what is it? A <u>day</u> or <u>two</u>?" Jack shot back.

"Hard to tell," said the monk with a puzzled look.

"What do you mean **special?**" Jack said. Of course I'm

going to meet somebody special. Everyone is special in his or her own way.

The monk said, "Oh, special like soulmate." Jack laughed. That's all he needed - to meet a soulmate after he had just finished deciding that he didn't need a woman in his life. Sorry, buddy. Poor timing. The monk was still standing there smiling. Hell, the monk didn't even look at the sticks. He was going to tell Jack what he told him no matter what those sticks said.

"OK," Jack said, "How will I know it is her?" That should pin his ass down pretty well.

The monk now appeared to be looking into his mind, then he said, "You will turn to the left, and she will be there. Any more questions?"

Not that Jack believed in fortune tellers, but just out of curiosity, he asked, "Is my book going to be published?" He had written a book that was ready for the press.

The monk pondered a moment and said, "Yes. Book published."

Jack asked, "Yeah? **When?**"

"Oh," he said, "maybe a couple years." A couple of years!! That's **not** what he wanted to hear. He was pissed at the thought of waiting that long. Jack totally discounted everything the monk said, after that, as he had discounted other fortune tellers.

Jack's soon-to-be ex-wife and he had gone to fortune tellers at the Jersey shore just for fun, and Jack never took much stock in what they said. After all, if it came true, so what? And if it didn't come true, so what? It was either going to happen, or it wasn't, anyway.

Elizabeth and Jack went back to his hotel. Jack was staying at a four star Japanese resort that consisted of individual houses on the beach that looked like little grass huts with grass and bamboo sides. However, when you went inside, it had an air conditioner and full bathroom facilities. Elizabeth was shocked that it was $50 a night. That translated into 1000 pisos, which would nearly pay half of her tuition in college.

That night some friends of Elizabeth's came to the hotel and Jack took them all to the dining room at the resort. They had a buffet that evening for $10 per person. This included all you could eat of lobster, shrimp, prime rib, and a variety of other dishes. Including Elizabeth's parents, there were ten of them. The bill came to about 2000 pisos or $100. Jack thought it was pretty inexpensive to feed 10 people. One of Elizabeth's friends saw the bill and got very upset, calling the waiter over. She argued with the waiter while Jack asked Elizabeth what it was about. Elizabeth said the girl was scolding the waiter for ripping him off. Finally they explained to her that the bill was correct and she ran outside crying. Elizabeth went after her.

Elizabeth's friend was upset because the bill had been more than her tuition to nursing school and she had dropped out due to lack of ability to pay. It was not within her reality to conceive that one mere meal could cost that much. Jack felt ashamed. He felt like such an indulgent American that he told Elizabeth to tell her friend that he would pay her tuition through school. After Elizabeth told her that, the girl looked at Jack suspiciously. Later Jack talked with her, and she told him that she had to turn down his offer because she was not that kind of girl. She said one of her friends had a Chinese businessman who helped her through school, but when he came to see her at her house, the whole neighborhood would talk. She was a girl with good Christian upbringing, and could not do that. Once Jack realized what she thought he was trying to say, he asked Elizabeth to tell her that he didn't want anything from the girl except good grades. He did not need a mistress.

After they straightened that out, Jack ended up offering to pay her tuition by sending the money to Elizabeth. Elizabeth would go to the school and sign her up. He felt so filthy rich. God, he loved this place.

The next morning, Jack woke up feeling Lela on his chest. She was not actually physically there, but he felt her presence.

Lela had been a very beautiful Muslim woman Jack had met on a plane to Singapore. He tried to shake the feeling. He didn't know what to do. He had not ever had anything like this happen to him before. He was a conservative man who had been with IPM for eighteen years. Jack gave it his best denial tactics, but he **really** felt Lela was there. Not only that, but Lela was talking to him. Not like hearing voices or any of that psychotic stuff, but Jack knew what she was thinking.

He flashed back to the first time he had met Lela. She had the kind of beauty that could take a man's breath away. It wasn't just her physical beauty, but the way she carried herself, and the way she spoke. The first time he saw her, she was getting on his plane with a **big** Chinese guy. Jack had a window seat. She sat next to him on the plane and the big Chinese guy sat next to her. Jack saw a diamond ring on her finger, so he assumed they were married.

During the plane ride, all three of them fell asleep. When Jack awoke, Lela was sleeping with her head and shoulders on his chest. First, he took her in with his eyes. God, she was strikingly beautiful! Then he looked over to see that the Chinese guy was turned his way, but asleep. Jack thought if the big guy woke up, it was going to be a very uncomfortable situation. Some Chinese are very possessive of their wives and certainly would not appreciate his wife sleeping on the chest of some Caucasian guy. Oh hell! What to do?

Jack started blowing on her hair hoping that would wake her up. It didn't. She snuggled up closer. And there was that mean looking Chinese guy who had only to open his eyes to sign Jack's death warrant. He didn't want to make any noise or any gross movements to wake up her husband. So with his only free hand, he started patting her hip. Soon, she woke up with a jolt and said she was sorry. Then she started talking to him at the same time the Chinese guy was waking up. Jack immediately said, "That's a nice ring you have." She told him it had been her mother's ring. Jack asked her how long she had been married, and she looked at the ring and then at him and said,"Oh no. I'm not married."

"I'm sorry," Jack said, "I thought **he** (the Chinese guy) was your husband."

"Oh no," she said in her beautiful voice, "He is my coworker."

During the rest of the plane trip, he and Lela got along famously. Jack ended up telling her all about his life, and she did the same. They exchanged addresses, but Jack never expected to hear from her. When he got to Singapore, there was a message for him from Lela that she would call later. She ended up calling him every day he was in Singapore and writing him when he got back to the USA. She said she could talk to him like no other and tell him things she could tell no other. They were writing regularly, and then after a while, her letters stopped coming. Jack kept writing, but there was no response.

Finally, one day, Jack received a letter from her address in Malaysia, but there was a different name on the return address. The letter was from her roommate, and inside the envelope were his three letters unopened and a newspaper article. The note from the roommate said that the article would explain everything, and that she was sorry. The newspaper article was about a terrible accident involving a truck and a car. It gave the names of the people in the accident, saying that Lela had been decapitated, and died instantly.

Jack couldn't understand the way he felt. Her death didn't seem real. He felt sorrow, like deep thunder coming up from the core of his being. He pushed it back in denial and went about his daily routine. He tried to minimize his feelings for Lela. After all, they didn't know each other that long, and they were from different worlds. Jack knew they had a strong connection, but he didn't really feel that connection was broken, somehow.

The next month, Jack received gifts from Lela. In his mailbox was a large package containing two scrolls of Malaysia, one map of the city of Kuala Lumpur, and one of the city of Penang. There were a calendar and some elegant stationery. There was a note from Lela saying that she would like to visit him when she came to New York. Jack asked the postman how it was possible that he could get this package a month after she died. The postman showed Jack that it had been shipped by sea and the delivery was slower. Jack went outside the post office into his parked car and wept.

So now, in Cebu, here was Lela, lying on his chest once more, just like in the plane. Jack was no damn psychic. He didn't even believe in that stuff but here was somebody contacting him from the other side. Jack was sure as hell not going to tell anyone about **this**. She communicated with him through feelings. She needed him. She was upset. Her life had ended too soon. She asked to be with him for a while. She knew Jack needed her too. Jack let her stay. She needed the security of his company for a time, then she would move on. Jack felt her with him. Just for the hell of it he asked her questions. "Are you my soulmate?"

She telepathed, "No, but I'm going to help you find her."

"I don't want to find a soulmate," relayed Jack, "Give me a couple of years."

"I can't stay that long," Lela relayed back. Jack felt the weight of her sadness, but he also felt her sense of humor through it all. Jack felt he must be crazy, because he didn't feel crazy and its those people who don't feel crazy ... that are the ones who have a real problem.

Jack's thoughts were interrupted when Elizabeth came knocking on his door. She had her nursing school drop-out friend with her who wanted to talk to him. Elizabeth left to give them privacy. (Lela tells him not to trust the girl.) The potential nurse tells him that she has two kids to support and that she didn't want to tell him this because she was ashamed that her husband left her for another woman. She says that she has no man and cannot get divorced because divorce is not allowed in the Philippines. She says she had a dream about him last night and is now attracted to him. If Jack wants to have a relationship with her, it is OK. (Lela lets him know emphatically, she doesn't like this woman.) The potential nurse says that Jack doesn't have to give the money to Elizabeth. Jack can send it to her directly, but she doesn't know how she can go to school and support her children too. She squirms sitting on the bed next to him. Her thigh touches his. His hormones flush his face. Something screams, "Give her whatever she wants!" (Lela laughs.) Jack chokes on his saliva and starts coughing. He asks her how much money she needs to go to school and support her children. She says she needs tuition and 300 pisos a week. ($30). Jack tells her that he might be able to manage that, but she doesn't need to repay him in any way. She looks at him directly and says in a husky Cebuian voice, "I want to."

The ego is back! She wants him. It turns him on so much when a woman wants him. Whew! His ego and his hormones start sizing her up sexually. Oh yes. A definite catch. A real notch in the belt. She takes his hand into her lap with a pretended shyness and starts thanking him for what she could never achieve without him. Jack would like to achieve some things with **her**. Just when Jack's hormonal superman is about to save her and get rewarded, some Clark Kent part of him interrupts and Jack hears himself saying, "OK. Would you like to have breakfast with us?" He reluctantly pulls her up by the hand, and they head for the door that Elizabeth is standing behind.

His ego threatens to punish him with a lot of regret, and they were off to breakfast.

Jack couldn't believe that he passed up the opportunity to make his best fantasies come true. Whatever had gotten into him? Jack was now a male slut with morals. What a conflict! Where the hell did these morals come from? Jack thought he had them on the back burner, and here they are jumping out in front of him. There had better be a heaven, or he was going to be really pissed.

It would turn out later that Jack would send Elizabeth

money to take directly to the school. Miss nursing school dropout would try to convince Elizabeth to give the money directly to her, because she had no intention of going to school after all. Faithful Elizabeth would return the money to him and explain that her friend wasn't really committed to a nursing career.

So Jack left Cebu for the good 'ol USA with a displaced female soul traveling with him who interrupted his thoughts occasionally, and rested on his chest. Jack asked Lela how long she was going to stay, because he had to address a lot of problems when he got home, and he could feel her sadness as a heavy weight. He told her that she really needed to move on to the afterlife soon for her own good. He didn't think it was healthy for a soul to be hanging out attached to a live person, and Jack didn't think it was healthy for a live person to hang out with someone who was dead. She reassured him that she wouldn't be with him very long. Jack started to think about missing Lela, and then caught himself. He knew she couldn't stay.

Hawaii

It's a long trip from Cebu to the USA, about fifteen hours by air. The biological clock gets all messed up. Twelve noon in Pennsylvania is twelve midnight in the Philippines. The body adjusts well to the trip to Asia and the time zone changes. But on the way back to the USA, the body says, "No way!"

On the way over to the Philippines, the plane followed the sun, so it seemed like one big long day. Now on the way back, they were going the opposite way, so they had a very short night. Jack sat next to a black man who was a cook for the navy going for his R&R. He was an interesting fellow, and they talked quite a bit. After dinner, the cook downed a few martinis, telling Jack that it was the only way he could sleep. The cook fell asleep just as it became dark outside.

Jack walked down the isle toward the bathroom and was standing in line when he saw a Filipino woman looking at him. She said hello, and he returned the greeting. They began to talk and then continued their talk after he came out of the bathroom. She currently lived in Hawaii with her second husband, who was originally from Boston. She had been married before, and widowed. She and her first husband had hosted a Filipino talk show in Manila. He had been killed in a small-plane crash. She asked Jack if he was going to stop over in Hawaii. He told her he was not. She said that if he paid only fifteen dollars, the airline would let him stay over. Jack said that he knew about that and had been through Hawaii a couple times already without stopping. He was interested in the more exotic out-back places, and it seemed to him that Hawaii was very commercialized. She said he just **had** to stop in Hawaii, even if just to say he had been there. She thought he would like it there. Jack wondered if she was coming on to him. (Lela said no.) Then the woman gave him the name of an inexpensive hotel and told him about a place he could rent a car for ten dollars a day. He ended up talking to her for a few hours until the sun came up again, then he went back to sit next to the cook.

The stewardesses had started serving breakfast, and the cook did not realize he had slept only for a few hours. "Rise and shine, honey! It's breakfast time!" mocked Jack.

"Jeezus!" the cook said, "Morning already? I feel like I only slept a couple hours." Jack just laughed.

The plane arrived in Hawaii at three in the afternoon and Jack found out that the next plane left at 9 in the morning the next day. He called the Waikiki Gatekeeper Hotel recommended by the Filipina and they gave him a better rate than he expected. (Lela told him the Filipino lady was steering him in the right direction.) Oh what the hell. One more adventure before he went back. He decided to stay overnight and see Hawaii, so he made reservations and paid his extra fifteen dollars to the airline.

He hopped onto one of the Tiki buses and headed for the rental car stands. When he got off the bus, he saw a rainbow. Then he turned and saw another rainbow on the opposite side of the horizon. He has been told since, that this is impossible. But he had looked at the two rainbows several times, since the sight was so unique. It made him feel welcome.

He got his ten dollar rental car, headed for the hotel, and checked in. He had only two items of clothing that were not wrinkled, a grey polyester shirt and black polyester pants. He showered, shaved, dressed, and hit the road. Jack toured Hawaii and found it to be as commercialized as he had thought, but yes, there was something about the place he liked. When it was dark, he headed back to the hotel and went to his room to have a cigar. The room had a little balcony where he migrated to smoke, and he could see all the tourists walking down below. He decided to go for a walk on the street next to the beach. He was intrigued by all the different types of people - Filipinos, Japanese, Koreans, Chinese, Australians, and locals of every color and race. It reminded him of a Star Trek film. Jack saw a beautiful black girl with blue eyes. The mainland Japanese tourists were made up and dressed to perfection.

After a time Jack was bored and decided to go into a nightclub called "Scruples". He was not a drinker and didn't usually frequent bars, but he decided to go in to listen to the music and watch people dance. When he was inside, he found it very crowded, with two or three people deep at the bar. He looked around and found two empty bar stools. "Why were they empty?" Jack wondered, "Did someone throw-up near these seats?" Jack went over to sniff it out and it was fine. It was almost as if the seats had been saved for him. He ordered a club soda and after he got it, he swivelled his seat toward the dance floor. There were all kinds of people there. They were a lively, club-sophisticated bunch and many of them danced expertly to the rock music. Jack felt enlivened by the beat. He could still feel Lela with him.

He turned once around to set his drink on the bar and went face to face with an Asian woman who was ordering a drink beside him on his left. She was wearing a nurse's uniform. Jack said, "Hello."

She gave him a dull short "Hi!" and looked over his shoulder toward the dance floor. It looked as if she was by herself, which is unusual for Asian women. They usually have friends with them. Jack was normally too shy to talk to women at bars, and he had never picked up a woman in a bar and since his decision to forget about women, it seemed he never would. He had the purity of intent which enabled him to talk to her, even though it was obvious that she wasn't excited about talking to him.

Jack said, "Are you a tourist, or are you local?" Again, her eyes never met his and she gave him another short dull answer while looking at some other guy over his shoulder. She thought, "Is this guy clueless? Maybe he thinks I would wear my nursing uniform on vacation? I guess this tourist couldn't come up with a better line."

"Local," she said.

Well Jack didn't really care. He wasn't attracted to her anyway, and Jack wasn't there to pick anybody up, so he kept talking to her. This was something Jack had never done before in this kind of situation. After a while, and a few more short answers, she looked at him more intently to size him up. She perceived him as this older guy with polyester pants and shirt. She continued to look at him disinterestedly, and then turned away with a look on her face that said, "Why am I wasting my time talking to **him**?"

Jack still wanted to meet one of the local people, and she happened to be right there, so Jack started asking her questions about her life in Hawaii. She started to talk to him, but stood in such a way as to send a message to the other guys that she wasn't really with him, and they could feel free to ask her to dance.

He wasn't sure exactly how it happened, but Jack would end up talking to her until closing time.

At one of their silent moments, Jack felt Lela give him a little spiritual hug and leave him.

The woman said her name was Malia and that she was a nurse on the surgical floor of one of the hospitals. Sure enough, her uniform had a little red and white name tag with the name "Malia" on it.

She asked him if he was married, probably thinking that would make him go away. He thought about it for a second. She might go away if he said yes. He thought of what Gale had said about lies that don't hurt anyone. Well, hell, he wasn't really married, divorced, separated, or single. So he lied and said, "Divorced." He didn't want anything except conversation, and he would never see her again anyway.

They talked about a lot of things. It was her birthday that day, and she was out alone. She had just gotten off her shift and her girlfriend was supposed to meet her there. It would turn out that her girlfriend had gotten lost and finally just went home.

The time went fast. Soon it was closing time. Jack asked Malia if she would like to come to his room just to talk. He reassured her that he would not try anything funny, and she looked at him as if to say "Of course you won't. Who would even think of **that?**"

Before they left, he asked her if she wanted to dance, since he felt he had deprived her of getting a dance all night. They were playing the last dance, and luckily, it was a slow contemporary Hawaiian song by the Cazimero Brothers. The music was beautiful and fitting for the tourists. They walked out to the floor and Jack was very sure to keep a proper distance while he danced with her. She sensed his rigidity and tried to make him more comfortable by moving in closer. The disc jockey made the dance longer and longer by playing add-ons. Jack was **very** comfortable with this woman. They moved around the floor as one. She sensed it too, and when the song ended, she made it a point to pull away immediately. How could she be turned on to **this** guy?

Then they went to his room and talked until four in the morning. She knew Jack had to catch a plane at nine AM, so she started to leave.

Then they kissed each other. A small kiss. There didn't seem to be a reason for it. It was how you would kiss someone you really liked. It happened unexpectedly for both of them ... but it was nice. They both made this semi-embarrassed throat clearing noise at the same time, and then looked away. Jack told her she could stay in the extra bed if she was tired, and she said fine. Then they kissed again and again and Jack felt the earth stir. Jack felt that he was **home** and had never been home before. His ego was non-existent. Jack was purely himself, and he and she were one soul. In a moment of clarity that was going to last forever, he knew he loved this woman in the purest way. There was no thought, just complete and utter knowing. He made love to her and with her. It wasn't thrilling or racy. It wasn't infatuation or conquering. It felt like old love that always was and always would be. It was the body and mind completely giving in to the mingling of souls. It was as if their two spirits rose out of their bodies and mingled above the bed, above the room, above the hotel, above the city, above the island, and above the earth. At one point Jack entered that room in her mind that houses her soul. Her soul was not aware that Jack was there, but he could feel her awakening. A song was playing on the radio: "With you I am born again."

The next morning Jack packed up his things and was out the door. He kissed her politely and he told her she could stay in the room and sleep if she wished. She looked confused as if she was saying to herself, "What am I doing here?" Jack got outside. "What am I doing?" he asked himself, "I just met someone, and for the first time in my life, I am in love. So now I'm going back to Pennsylvania?" Had he fallen in love with a one night stand? Yet there was something inside him that told him everything would work out. He knew he would see her again.

He reluctantly drove to the airport. When he got to the ticket counter, there was no agent there. There were only a couple people on the sidelines and no line. Everything seemed so surreal, yet he knew that it was supposed to be the way it was. He was not a believer in fate, yet at this moment he totally accepted it.

An Australian saw him standing there with his suitcases. He shouted with a friendly laugh, "Hey mate, the airlines are on strike! You can't get off the island!" Jack quickly called the hotel. Could they take him back in the same room he had last night? Yes, they could. He went back to the hotel. She was gone. He called the surgical floors in all three hospitals in Hawaii. No one claimed to know a Malia who worked second shift. Could she have misled him? Jack waited until after four PM and called the hospitals again. Still, no one said they knew a Malia on second shift on the surgical floor. His mind was panicking like it always did when he needed to solve a problem right away, but there was something inside of him that knew everything would work out. This feeling gave him a peacefulness he had never experienced before.

Then his phone rang. Who could be calling him? It must be the hotel. Jack picked up the receiver and said, "Hello."

Malia answered back, "Hello?" Jack had told her he would be <u>gone</u>.

"Why did you call?" Jack asked, wonderfully amazed.

"I don't know," she said. Jack asked her if she knew the airlines were on strike.

She said, "No. I just woke up." Jack asked her to dinner. She said she had to work that night, but invited Jack to the Queen's hospital cafeteria.

He met Malia at the hospital that night for dinner. They agreed that she would come to visit him after work. After dinner, Jack bought a cake for her and waited for her to finish work. They celebrated her birthday at the hotel. She told him that she was upset about what had happened the night before. She had never gone to a bar alone before, she had never picked up a guy in a bar, and she had never had a one-night stand before. She was confused, as to why she had done these uncharacteristic things. Jack just smiled and said, "We all do things we don't understand."

She stayed with him again that night, not understanding her uncharacteristic actions. Then she left for home the next day to get some sleep before work.

The next day, Jack found out that the airlines would likely be on strike for a week. Jack called his boss at IPM in Princeton and said, "Ed. I know you are not going to believe this, but I am stuck in Hawaii. They are having an airline strike and I can't get off the island." There was a long pause at the other end of the line and then Jack heard Ed's envious voice say, "Callahan, you lucky son of a bitch. I'm not giving you time off. You are going to have to use your over accumulated vacation days for this. Hell, it's about time you had a vacation, anyway"

"OK, Ed."

The next night while Malia was working, Jack sat in his hotel room, trying to remember what a Chinese fortune teller had told him in Singapore a year prior. Jack had been working with a pretty Chinese woman in Singapore, and she had talked him into going to see this Chinese fortune teller who was supposed to be the "best in all of Asia". After dinner they went to find him, and she saw him sitting outside the Buddhist temple in his neighborhood. He was a very old man with white hair and one blind blue eye. He was a very charming charismatic man. Love seemed to emanate from his presence. The Chinese woman translated for Jack, since the fortune teller did not speak English. The old man told Jack jokingly that he had been blessed with one eye to see the world and another eye to see the spirit. He had impressed Jack with the way he had answered his questions. The young woman had asked the fortune teller if Jack was going to meet his soulmate. Then the old man had stared at Jack as if looking right through him. The fortune teller nodded, yes, as if in a trance. Jack thought the beautiful Chinese woman was playing with him, so he joined in the flirting. It had not seemed important what the fortune teller told him back then, but now Jack was trying to remember what the old man predicted, so he started writing it down to help his memory process. Perhaps some spirit helper was moving his pen when he wrote the following dialogue and called it ...

What Do You Say to a Soulmate?

What do you say to a soulmate? Do you stammer with the fear of losing her?

    No, I think not. Once found, it would be as if she always was and always will be. No fear of loss.

Do you have to get her attention?

    If she is your soulmate, she will know somewhere within herself who you are. It won't take much.

Will I know immediately who she is?

    There will be a mist surrounding her, but it will lift in time.

Is it possible to blunder and lose her?

    Not if you are ready.

What if **she** is not ready?

    You are soulmates. If you are ready, she is ready.

Will things be perfect between us?

Being human is not perfect, so the answer is no. But, down deep in your soul you will be able to accept the imperfections more than with any other.

Will I ever be the same again?

Yes. The same. And more. Finding your soulmate does not change you. You find her **because** you have already changed into who you really are.

Will she be beautiful?

To you? Of course.

It sounds like nothing will change though. Won't it be a magnificent fantasy come true?

It is subtle and moving, but it is not a "high"or a fantasy. And over time, yes, it is magnificent but not the **WAY** you THINK.

What way would it be?

The "way" in Chinese is different than the English word. English <u>change</u> their behavior to what suits them. They change their words. You can't <u>change</u> the way you think. It requires a <u>transformation</u>. You are born whole, then life "changes" you. Follow this closely. The <u>way</u> you think is transformed following the transformation of your <u>self</u>, into the person you were born to be.

Isn't it like finding a missing part to make me whole?

No. If you are not already whole, then you are not ready. There is a part of you that you have prepared. It is finished, but uninhabited.

Same for her?

Yes. It is the "us".

OK, so where do I find her?

You are asking the wrong question. The question is When?"

Alright, **when** do I find her?

When you are ready, she will be there.

What if I want to meet her **now**? What if I need to meet her **now**?

Then you are not ready. As soon as you are whole enough not to be desperate ... not to need her ... then she will be there.

I'm beginning to see it now. So, then what profound thing can I say to my soulmate when I meet her?

By the time you have gone through the desperateness and the loneliness and everything you need to go through and you have become your own person ... the most profound thing you can say is, "Hello."

It had been fun, and Jack had been impressed with the fortune teller's wisdom in his answers. He had applied it to his relationship with Lynn at the time. He had hoped that he and Lynn would be "ready" soon. He asked him the price for the reading? The old man refused monetary payment, saying that Jack would be paying a price, but not to him. He told Jack that he would someday come back to Singapore after this had all come to pass, and then he could pay him ... a visit. Jack had looked at the old man and tried to calculate how old he was (70? 80?). As if reading his mind, the old man laughed and said, "As you can see. It won't be that long." They all laughed.

Later that night, the Chinese woman suddenly turned to Jack and said, half-joking, half-serious, "Hello!" Jack just smiled at her. She was very beautiful, but no.

Now in his hotel room in Hawaii, Jack read what he had just written. It made sense! Everything made sense! He thought back to his talk with Gale about limits. Malia was twenty-five exactly the night he met her. Coincidence? There was a double rainbow that day, supposedly an impossible phenomenon. A sign? Lela had left after he was with Malia. Lela promised she would help him find his soulmate. Did she? The airlines were unexpectedly on strike! Malia had **never** been to a bar by herself except for the night she met Jack. Then there was the Buddhist monk in Cebu saying he would meet her in a "day or two". And yes, he had crossed over the international date line! "Hard to tell" whether it was one day or two. And yes, he had turned to the left and she was there. Could this all be coincidence? But then there was the undeniable feeling of being home when he was with her. There was the undeniable feeling that he was in love with her. How could he be? He didn't believe in love at first sight, yet he knew her. He had made love to her without even thinking about sex. And he didn't feel like he had "fallen" in love. It felt more like he had been in love with her forever. How could this be?

He decided to conduct a test. OK God. If this is real, then I'll flip "heads" on a coin. He took out a quarter and flipped it. It was heads. No, wait. That is only a fifty-fifty chance. No, I'll flip "heads" three in a row. Heads! Heads! I'll tell you what. If this is real, I will see a shooting star in the next minute. Jack went out on the balcony and looked into the sky. It didn't take a minute. As soon as he walked out, there it was, a definite, definite, vivid, long-lasting shooting star. The hair on the back of his neck stood up. He didn't breathe for a long time.

He saw himself standing on the balcony. There he was; a cynical 38 year old, normally clueless man, who thought coincidences were coincidences, did not believe in fate, and did not believe in love at first sight. Should he ask for one more sign? No. He did not want to piss God off. After all, what if God had arranged the stopover, the double rainbow, the coordination of an unlikely meeting between two unlikely people, the airplane strike, and the shooting star ... and Jack **still** questioned it?!

One more thing Jack realized. Something had sneaked up on him. Jack was happy. Maybe his dad had bribed God. If so, thanks Dad! At that moment, Jack stopped trying to figure it out. He shifted from thinking to knowing. It really was the way it was. He had met his soulmate. He was in love. He was happy. He knew.

"Exactly," he heard Dr. Mintz say in his mind. Then Dad's echo, "Be happy Jack" and Betty, "Be happy Jack." And the smiling Chinese monk, "You look to the left, and she is there", and Lela, "I'll help you find your soulmate." Just then, lightening crackled outside, followed by a big boom. Jack supposed it was God's way of saying, "Don't piss me off, Jack. I've already gone to a lot of trouble for you." . The lightening seemed like one of God's exclamation points.

Malia came by that night, and they talked. She seemed distraught. She began, "I want you to know I have never done anything like this before. I've never slept with anyone on the first date. I've never gone out by myself before. I don't know what's happening to me. I don't even **know** you!"
He listened. He smiled.
"Jack, I feel like I do know you, but how could I? It doesn't make sense!"
Jack smiled again, "Well, so much for Chinese logic."
She smiled and then her forehead wrinkled again, "But Jack, you don't really fit into my life. You are not Chinese. You are not a doctor. You don't even fit the physical profile for any Caucasian guy I might be attracted to. You are not blonde. You are not athletic. My god! You wear polyester! How can this be?"
Jack said simply, "I don't know. When do I meet your parents?"
Her mouth dropped. She looked at him in disbelief. She fought with her logic. She sat there perplexed.

He went over to her to comfort her, and the next thing they knew, they were making love again. "I can't believe I'm doing this," she said, "Only Caucasian girls do this. They throw their lives away for some poor older divorced guy." Jack searched for something to defend himself with.

"I'm not really poor," he said, "I have several houses and I'm probably worth $250,000!" She laughed hard as she was taking his shirt off.

"Oh my God," she snickered, "That's only a down payment on a house in Hawaii. You think that is a lot?"

"In Pennsylvania it is," he said, removing her blouse.

They made love and the center of the universe was room 2429 in the Waikiki Gatekeeper hotel in the city of Honolulu in the state of Hawaii, USA, planet earth. "I love you," he said, **sure** for the very first time in his life.

With tears and reluctance in her eyes, she said, "I love you too."

Afterwards, she asked, "Do you want to come to church with me tomorrow?"

"Do we have to?" he said, thinking of other things they could be doing instead.

"Yes," she said, "I'm teaching Sunday School."

"My God! She is a Sunday School teacher. I slept with a Sunday School teacher!" feigning shock. He rubbed it in. "I'm going to hell for sure!"

She jumped on him tickling, him ruthlessly. "Don't you dare say anything about the way we met or anything we've been doing," she screamed with laughter. "Do you hear?" Then she thought for a moment, as if making a decision about something. She said with a frugal thought, "Turn in your rental car. We will use mine. It will save money."

He asked jokingly "What if you get cold feet and decide to abandon me?" She looked at him with her Chinese logic and decided it was a fair and practical question.

"Rent another one," she smiled.
They made plans to go to church and then to the beach. She went home that night to get a little sleep and dress for church the next day.

In the morning, Jack's telephone rang. It was Malia. He went to the lobby to meet her. They walked to her RX7 and started for church. "Nice car," he said.

"Yes," she replied, "my dad thinks it is a little extravagant, but he is 100% Chinese, and I am half Korean, thanks to my mother. Here in Hawaii, Chinese is associated with the word 'pake'(pronounced 'pakay'), which means frugal."

"So," he said, "which part of you decided to pick me up? The Chinese part, or the Korean part?" She glanced over at him.

"Neither. I really struggled with it this morning. Both parts said no. Family and friends are very important to Asians, you know. And here I am taking someone I just met to church, to meet them. But once they see you, they won't think anything of it. They will think I am working on my next convert. They know me and my preferences. They won't even imagine that I am actually seeing someone like you," she smiled smugly.

The church service was wonderful. Jack had been raised Catholic, with the priest holding mass in Latin. He had fallen asleep nearly every time he had gone to church as a kid. This church was different. They sang songs and the minister was a charismatic man who actually made good sense out of the Bible. Jack was impressed.

After the service, Malia introduced Jack to her parents. Her father was a reserved, but friendly man. Her mother was a bright smiling woman with wide-wing glasses. Neither were much bigger than a Filipino. But then Jack met Malia's brothers. They were both about six feet tall and looked like linebackers for the University of Hawaii. They were friendly enough, but Jack wondered what they would think if they knew he was in love with their sister. Then Jack met Malia's friends. She really was a Sunday School teacher! She was active in the church. He would have felt guilty for sleeping with her except that he knew he loved her.

After church, Malia and Jack went to the beach and spent the day together. Jack was happy and content for the first time in a very long time. The sun was warm, the sky was blue, and the air was fresh. The Japanese tourists were perfectly dressed, including the women in their bathing wardrobes with wide brim hats to block the sun from their perfectly made up faces. The little Japanese kids were well behaved and cute as ever with their wide-eyed almond eyes. Friendly locals of every size, shape, color, and race covered the beach. The surf boarders rode the ocean waves, and swimmers were jumping off a huge piece of lava rock into the water.

Lying on the beach with Malia at his side, a thought

suddenly invaded his contentment: He had lied to Malia! Oh no! He told her he was divorced in the bar! Should he tell her the truth, now? He wanted to be open and honest with her ... except for this. No. He was **not** going to risk losing her. He would go home, move out, get a divorce, and she would never know the difference. Yes, that was it. He would tell her the truth after he had moved out. It had been a stupid lie, not meant to harm anyone, but now it was a thorn in his side. What would she do if she knew? He didn't want to think about it. He looked at her lying next to him. God she was beautiful! He hadn't really noticed her beauty before. What did he have to give her? Nothing. But, he was **not** going to give her up. Just the thought of it made him feel despair.

She opened her eyes and caught him looking at her. "Why are you feeling sad?" she asked. He was taken aback.

"How do you know I'm feeling sad?" he said.

"Your eyes tell me everything," she said, "It's easy to see." But how did she know? He thought it was hard to see through his defenses to his feelings.

"I have been told, I am stoic," he said, sitting back.

"Hey," she said, "all Chinese are stoic, but not really. I know how you feel every minute. Like now, you are scared."

"I'm not scared," defended Jack immediately. She raised her eyebrow and looked at him, giving him a chance to get in touch with it.

"OK," he shook his head in amazement, "I am scared to be with someone who can read my mind."

She smiled, "I'm not reading your mind, just your feelings."

"God!" he said. "Is this a Chinese thing? I mean, do you read everyone's feelings that well?"

She pondered a moment and said, "Not really. You are just easy."

Jack used this to his advantage, saying, "So then, you must know I really do love you."

She caught on right away. "No, Jack. I just know you feel love for me. But love is not just a feeling." Jack knew she was right technically, in her conservative, realistic Chinese logic.

He also knew he loved her.

He started explaining to her (and to himself) that he didn't believe in love at first sight, but perhaps he had been hasty in adopting this perspective, or this was just an exception. Since he had been studying the subject for so long, he was now able to see it much better than when he was 21.

"Perhaps," she said.

They lay back down on the beach and Jack's insecure mind started looking for an edge, something that would make him preferable. After all, she would eventually find out he had no personality, and he had a stupid sense of humor. Lynn had found this out right away. Then, it hit him. He said as nonchalantly as he could, "What if I become famous one day. Would you be able to handle being with a famous person? You see, I've written this book and it is going to be a best seller. Not because of my ego, but because it really is a good book that will help a lot of people."

She surprised him by saying, "I don't know if I would like that. It may change your personality."

"Change my personality?" thought Jack. "What personality?" He was also disappointed that this was not an edge.

She went on. "I like you as you are. You Haoles (Hawaiian for 'Caucasian') have too much ego. Just be yourself. It is enough."

"Look," confessed Jack, "I am really stoic, I have no personality, and I have a dumb sense of humor. I mean, that's really the way I am. I'm a boring guy."

She looked at him as if getting a little bored and frustrated and said, "I am a good judge of people. I know you. I know you are trying hard to impress me and trying to be different than you are, and when you do that, it bores me. You take yourself so seriously. If you keep it up, I will have to stab you in the ribs with my finger." She made like she was going to tickle him, and he jumped.

"OK! OK!" he said, laughing nervously. "I'll stop taking myself seriously."

Then she motioned for him to lie down and put his head in

her lap. He did, and she ran her fingers through his hair. It was the very most sensual thing she could have done. It was the one sensual thing Jack loved the most. He could be calmed easily by someone running her fingers through his hair ... and it had been so long. He felt free enough to fall asleep.

When he awoke, she was still caressing him. He looked at her with the sun behind her and remembered his dream when he was fourteen. It was her. He knew it. She bent down and kissed him. Tears of happiness ran down his face. She knew the little boy inside him.

She didn't even ask why he was crying. With the exception of his dad's death, he hadn't cried in years, let alone with anyone present. She just wiped his tears with her thumb, totally accepting.

All week Malia would struggle with her Chinese logic and her heart. She listened to her heart and this love she kept experiencing, but then she would start to feel confused when she was not with Jack. By the end of the week, the airlines had gone back to work and Jack was able to schedule a flight out.

On their last day together, Jack rented a motorcycle and they went off to explore the other side of the island. During the motorcycle ride, Jack felt her hug him and rest the side of her face against his back in the most loving way.

They stopped at a deserted beach and laid the towels out on the beach. They lay facing each other, and Jack said emptily, "You know, I have nothing to give you. If there were some dragons around, I'd slay them for you, but it looks like the white knights have already killed them off."

She smiled at him with the wisdom of a grandmother, "I don't need anything, but maybe there are some dragons you can slay, Jack. They are your dragons. Can you slay them for me?"

"Well," he said seriously, "What do these dragons look like?"

"The one I see," she bemused, "is very serrriousss. He thinks too much. In fact, never mind killing him. I will kill him, right now!" She jumped on Jack and started tickling him unmercifully. They rolled around laughing until Jack finally got on top of her and held her hands down. Suddenly, her voice changed and she yelled vehemently, "Get off me!!! Get off me, I said!!" He let her up and she punched him in the arm and walked away down the beach.

He went after her, following at a safe distance, and said, "Maybe you do have a dragon or two." She turned around and looked at him. The adrenaline was still coursing through her body. She was still angry and also embarrassed by her own behavior. He approached her and she hit him with her towel, regretting it as she did it. He asked, "Did anyone ever hold you down like that?" She reached for him and burst into tears.

"Yes," she cried, and held him tightly to her for a long while.

"It's OK now," comforted Jack. "It's over now." He waited until she calmed down and said, "You know, I really do love you." Her sense of humor returned.

"Sure you do," she smiled, "You Haoles fall in love easily. That's why there is so much divorce and you cheat on your wives. Chinese are different. We believe love is a slow process."

"I must be Chinese, then," he said, "Because that's what I believe too. So when I say I love you, it goes against all my upbringing and beliefs and that shocks me, But you know what really shocks me?"

"Tell me," she said warily.

Then, he said with the utmost assuredness, "I know that you love me too."

She looked at him as if he had dispelled her best kept secret. Then she retorted, "We Chinese are logical. Yes, we have feelings like anyone else, but we are taught to have common sense and think things through before letting out feelings that may lead to compulsive behavior. It doesn't fit with my logic that you and I could love each other yet."

"Yes, I know," he said. "It doesn't make sense at all. But it's true. I know it. You know it. And I know you know it." She flinched.

"We will see," she said, giving in just a little, but knowing at that moment he was right.

Their goodbye was simple. At the moment they said goodbye, they both knew they were meant for each other and would be together again.

Pennsylvania

On the flight back, Jack had time to think about all that had happened. He thought about the monk in Cebu and the double rainbow. He thought about Lela saying goodbye after he had met Malia. He thought about the dream he had when he was fourteen. He thought about the "coincidences". He knew beyond the shadow of a doubt that there had been no coincidences. Malia was his soulmate.

Then he felt scared. What did he have to give her? Nothing! There was nothing he could save her from. She had a nice car, a good job, and a nice family. How could he keep her? She said she loved him, but was confused about it. If he wasn't there, maybe her Chinese logic would take over, and what would she do? She wasn't <u>sure</u> like Jack was.

Then his thoughts turned to Pennsylvania. No matter what happened with Malia, he was going to move out. He had already decided that. As soon as he got back, he would get his things and find somewhere to go.

When Jack arrived home, the first thing he was going to say was, "I'm moving out." He caught a limo from the airport and it dropped him off in front of the Newtown house. He opened the door to see his wife crying. She sobbed, "My father died last night."

He saw the pain in her face. She had been closest with her father. He couldn't desert her now. He mentally postponed his plans to move out, and made himself available to her.

Jack was there for his wife during the funeral. Later that month, they took their usual vacation at the New Jersey shore with his brother-in-law's family.

He kept in touch with Malia by phone. He had installed his own phone in his room. Malia's Chinese logic was in full force. Her doubt was stronger now that Jack wasn't with her. She wanted to be friends, but she wanted to date others. She had talked about Jack with her closest friends and they all agreed that she should see others. A long-distance relationship was too difficult, and there were too many differences in race, culture, and religion. There was a Chinese doctor who was interested in her. She was honest with Jack but he could tell by her voice she was torn. Jack began to doubt that it had all been real. Maybe she wasn't his soulmate. He couldn't feel himself being that concerned or jealous about her dating others. Maybe it had all been a delusion.

One day at the shore, Jack was walking alone and pondering all this, asking himself if had all been real. He looked up, and saw a double rainbow emanating behind two sides of a cloud.

That night he went with Lynn to the usual New Jersey shore psychic, as they did every year. She saw them both and told them they would have no financial problems over the year. She said their relationship was strained and asked to see them separately. When Lynn went in, the psychic told her there would be a divorce. When Jack went in, she told him he had met his soulmate, and that they would be together. In his usual psychic-cynic way, he said "Yeah, when?"

She said "Oh, a couple of years." Jack was not ready to hear that! But because of his previous experiences, he had a little more curiosity than usual. He asked her why. She said that he needed to take care of some family matters and he was not ready to be with his soulmate yet. Jack rebelled. "I am ready" he said. She said no, he wasn't ready. He had to be reborn. Jack thought to himself, "Here we go again. I'm not good enough yet. I'm tired of not being good enough. To hell with this!" The psychic also told Jack that he had hurt his true love with a lie. "Hmmmm," thought Jack, "Not if I can help it."

He paid the psychic and walked out. He was acting uncharacteristically pissed off, and his wife asked him what his problem was. He told her that the psychic didn't know what the hell she was talking about. Lynn said, "I had a bad reading too."

They returned from the shore and continued to live in separate rooms. Meanwhile, Jack looked for a house. He called Malia regularly. She wanted to be ... just friends. But she assured him that she was not sleeping with anyone. The Chinese doctor was seeing her, playing tennis with her, and pursuing her. Jack did not feel jealous, oddly. At first he thought maybe it was because he didn't care as much as he thought, but no, it wasn't that. He was just <u>sure</u> they would be together, someday. Odd.

Then one day, Lynn looked through his room and found his telephone bill. She called Malia's number in Hawaii. Because of the time difference, she woke Malia up in the middle of the night. She introduced herself as "Jack Callahan's wife". She talked to Malia for a while to size her up. She learned that Malia had good Christian values and used that to skew the picture. She asked Malia, "Did you sleep with my husband?" Malia was filled with shame and admitted she did, but told Lynn she hadn't realized Jack was married. Lynn acted very forgiving and told Malia that they were having problems, but they were not going to get a divorce. She made it seem as if they were happily married other than having a little tiff at the present time. She requested, "I really wish you would not interfere."

Malia was devastated. She felt betrayed by Jack. He had lied to her. He had duped her into having affair with a married man, knowing her values! How could she be so stupid? How could Jack do that to her? He had made her break a strict code of ethics. She didn't ever want to talk to him again. She called the Chinese doctor and asked him if she could come to his apartment. She slept with him that night, trying to obliterate all connections with Jack Callahan.

Later that day, Jack arrived from work and his wife asked, "Who is Malia?" Jack said it was none of her business.
Lynn said, "It is now. I'm going to take you for everything you are worth. I'm getting a good Philadelphia lawyer and you are going to end up with nothing."

The next day, Jack told Gale about what had happened. Gale said that she had been thinking about renting out a room in her big house and invited him to think about it. That night, Jack moved his things out of Newtown into Gale's house. He tried to get Malia on the telephone many times, but he kept getting her answering machine. She did not want to talk to him.

Limbo (the Cocoon)

So there was Jack, his soulmate having gone off with the man of her Chinese logic, and it was his fault. He was burdened by heavy guilt for not being honest with her, and he longed to make it up to her. He was acutely aware of his own hurt, but he needed to help her with her pain even more. But how could he help her now? She wouldn't even talk to him. This was on his mind day after day. And it seemed that every time he turned on the radio, the song "Broken Wings" was playing. He didn't know what to do.

About that same time a huge tree root arrived for him by international overnight mail. He had been so caught up in things that he had forgotten about Elizabeth, the Dumagats, and the tree root extract that took hunger away for a whole day. Jack had no idea what to do with the root just as he had no idea what to do with Malia. He didn't know if he **could** do anything with the root or with Malia. In an act of desperation, he put the large root in the microwave and listened as it made strange sounds. He cooked it until he could smell wood burning and then took it out and split it with his axe. All he got was a steaming piece of wood, split in half. It looked like it was going up in smoke, like his relationship with Malia. Why didn't he just get the extract sent? He had just thought of it. He could have gotten the substance itself and saved fifty dollars to ship it. Aw what the hell, he wasn't interested in the root anymore anyway. Clearly, he thought, his approach to things in general didn't work that well. It was hard to be "Jack".

That made him think. He decided to do something out of character. He decided to be obnoxious. Malia needed to unload her pain and he was going to provide an opportunity for her to do it. He started calling her every day. She never picked up the phone, so he left a message on her answering machine every day . It was a simple message just saying that he would like to talk to her. After a week or so, one day he started leaving a message when the receiver raised and hung up. She was there! It gave him an oddly good feeling to realize that she was interacting with him even in a negative way. He paused, took a deep breath, and then dialed again. Her line was busy. He wondered if she would think he was stalking her, but decided to keep dialing her number. It was busy each time he tried and it was two hours later when her phone rang at the other end.

The answering device picked up with a different message this time. It said, "Hi, there's no one to take your call right now, so please leave your name, telephone number, and message ... unless you are a pathological liar ... and we know who he is. So if you are him, just hang up and don't ever call here again." When he heard this message Jack paused in a bit of shock, then the voice activated answering device hung up on him after he was silent for the alloted maximum time.

After a time, Jack hit the redial button on his phone and Malia's answering device provided the same message. This time Jack answered, "This is the pathological liar. I just thought you may have some things you would like to say to me, and I thought I would give you one last chance to say them ... out of the goodness of my heart (provoking her) ... to provide closure ... you know ... because some women don't get to tell off guys who hurt them ... and it may save you some money for therapy later and ..."

Click! Malia picked up the phone.

She was pissed. "Is this some sort of sick joke to torment me? Don't say another word you bastard! If you interrupt me, I will hang up immediately and change my number so I never have to listen to your rotten bullshit lies again. You are going to sit there and not talk. Do you understand?! DO YOU?!"

"Yes," said Jack.

"First of all," she said, "You made me commit adultery. Because of your lies, I went to bed with a married man. You made a fool of me. I introduced you to my friends and family. I am so ashamed. You deceived me. I hope you are happy, you bastard. I hope you got what you want. What, did you want, to see what it was like to lay a Chinese girl? Well, now you know, so leave me the hell alone. I can't believe I was actually starting to fall for your bullshit. Something told me there was something weird about you." She paused. Then she started to cry "You hurt me, Jack. You really hurt me. How could you do that?" She paused again and Jack's eyes welled up with tears. He could feel her pain. How **could** he have done that?

Then she was pissed again, "Listen you damn liar." (She only cursed when she was the at very peak of emotion). "If you care at all, you won't call me again. (Now hurt) I can't take it. Please, please don't call me anymore. I'm back with Brad (The Chinese doctor) and if you keep bothering me, you could ruin it. You got what you wanted. (Not really, thought Jack) Now please just leave me alone. Brad is everything I ever wanted in a man. Can you understand that?"

"Yes," answered Jack. "Is there anything else you want to tell me?"

"Well, what do you want to hear?" she said obnoxiously,

"Do you want to hear how great Brad is in bed? Once I realized how filthy you made me, I had to get rid of it somehow, and Brad was there for me. In fact, when you called, Brad was here and we were in bed together. That's why I took the phone off the hook. In fact, he just left. So I'm pretty tired right now and I'm not in any mood to put up with any more of your shit. And don't worry about any future therapy bills. Brad is all I need to wash you away. You were just a small interruption in my life. I'll get over it. You were just a fling that a lot of women have and then live to regret. Maybe it humbled me some to know that I made such a mistake. Once I get you off this phone, I am going to get on with my life. So get off the phone."

"I'm sorry," said Jack (holding back the tears).

"I'm sorry too," she said. "I'm sorry I ever met you."

She hung up and then they both cried alone for a long time.

Over the next six months, Jack bought and moved into a house. He started divorce proceedings and filled his life with work. After a few months, Gale tried to introduce him to one of her friends. He declined the offer, and said he wasn't interested. Gale noticed that there was something different about Jack. He was lonely, but he had a peace about him. He was not interested in pursuing women.

She said to him one day "Hey, you know that redhead is going to be 25 soon."

Jack smiled and said "No thanks. I have other things I have to do."

"C'mon Jack," she said, "All work and no play makes Jack a dull boy."

"Am I that dull?" he asked.

"Not to me," she said, "but maybe to yourself. What are you doing with yourself these days?"

He told her that he was getting his finances in order and looking into a new career.

"What about love, Jack?" she asked.

"I get plenty of love from you, Gale. You love me, don't you?" he smiled.

"Sure," she replied, "I love ya. But don't you miss getting laid once in a while?"

"Well, to be honest," he confided, "there is only one person I want to make love with."

"Oh God," said Gale shaking her finger at him, "that Hawaiian girl."

"She's Chinese," he said simply.

Gale gave him the hairy eye ball. "You! You?! Are lovesick? Not YOU Jack."

"I wouldn't call it lovesick," he said. "I'm just different now."

"I noticed," she said with a worried look. "Have you ever felt this way before?"

"Not in all the years I have been alive," he said. "You know. It's kind of weird in a way. I feel good just knowing who she is and that she is alive somewhere in the world. And I feel lonely. Very lonely. The loneliest I have ever felt. Even lonelier than I felt in my marriage, but I can handle it better somehow. I only feel lonely for her."

He looked over at Gale, and she was wiping her eye. He cocked his head and looked at her questionly. In a rare moment, he had caught her displaying emotion, and she was embarrassed. Gale quickly switched to her tough act.

"So she ruined you for all other women?" Gale leaned forward.

"You could say that," he mused.

"You dumb ass," Gale berated. "You're in love. I can't believe you really are. Not only that, but you are **hopelessly** in love. So what are you going to do ... mope around the rest of your life?"

"I don't know," explained Jack. "It's not important right now. Only my career and my job are important right now."

"So," glared Gale. "What about Jack? Is **Jack** important? How about Jack, Doctor Co-'dip'endent? What does Jack want? Not co-dependent Jack, but the inner Jack."

"There will be plenty of time for me later," he responded.

"Call her," commanded Gale.

"I can't," said Jack. "Promised I wouldn't."

"Then," leered Gale, "Break your promise. Call her. Then apologize for breaking your promise."

"I can't," said Jack. "I'd be breaking my word."

"Break your word," said Gale stubbornly.

"Listen you," said Jack, half-jovial, half-serious. "You were the one who told me to lie. I did. And look where it got me. She hates me now."

"She can't hate you for that unless she loved you to begin with. Besides, don't blame me for what you did. That's your responsibility. Just shut up and call her."

"No, Gale. I can't hurt her again," said Jack adamantly.

"Yes you can," said Gale looking serious, but with a glint in her eye.

Jack laughed, "You are so evil, Gale."

Jack stewed all that night, staring at the phone. Finally, he picked it up and dialed.

Malia answered the phone, "Hello?"

"Hi," said Jack in a voice that was barely audible and barely recognizable, even to himself.

There was a long silence, and then Malia said, "Hello, Jack."

"Are you busy?" he asked. There was another long silence.

"Not at this minute," she replied. He waited for her to say, "Why are you calling me?" She didn't.

"I just wanted to call (he searched for words) to see how you were doing." Another silence.

"I'm fine," she said.

"I still feel bad about what I did to you," said Jack.

"I've already forgiven you," she said. "It humbled me, and I needed that. I was getting caught up too much in my own desires."

"I hope you don't hate me," he said. "I have never hurt anyone like that before, and you, of all people, would be the last person I would want to hurt."

"I'm sorry too," she said, "for some of the things I said to you. It wasn't very Christian of me."

At this point, Jack was overwhelmed with joy just by the mere fact he was interacting with her. He was walking around his bedroom with the telephone making all kinds of happy silent gestures while trying to maintain a sober voice on the phone.

"It's OK. I can't blame you. How is everything going?" he said. Now he was silently jumping up and down making victory signs with his free hand. He lost his balance and fell to the floor making a noise.

"It is really good," she said. "My job is going well. I got a big raise, and Brad and I are planning our wedding. What's that noise?"

He regained his composure, practically flying off the floor. "Congratulations," he said, trying to be happy for her.

"Thank you," she said. "You know, I did enjoy talking with you. You are a very interesting person."

"Can we be friends?" Jack said politely. He was cringing as he waited for a negative answer.

There was that silence again, and then she said, "OK, But no more lies."

"OK," said Jack, "I promise. That is ... I guess a promise from a liar doesn't mean that much, so maybe I should just say OK."

She laughed a little.

They began talking, and ended up staying on the phone for two hours. Jack made it a point never to talk about anything romantic, but just to be her friend.

Jack told her about a house he was having a hard time unloading. He was just sick of this house and wanted to get rid of it. She said, "Maybe God doesn't want you to sell the house."

"I don't believe God gets involved in real estate," Jack said.

Jack tried to explain all the details of his lie, and how it was never supposed to hurt anyone. She cut him off. It was too painful for her. He changed the subject to his current situation and she listened to him, as a friend.

She told him about her life. She was going to run the Tinman Triathlon and she was training for it. Her job was going well and he listened to her tell him of a few problems she was having with some co-workers' jealousy. By the time they hung up, they both felt better.

The next day Jack went to work wearing a big grin. Gale saw it and said, "Feel better now, Doctor?"

Jack finally sold the house he was trying to unload. Thirty days after he sold it, a realtor offered $34,000 more than the purchasers paid for it, and they sold it. Twenty days after that, the realtor sold it to a developer for $30,000 more than that. Jack told Malia this, and she said that he should have more faith in God, and not try to be so willful. If Jack had held onto the house for 50 more days, a developer would have come knocking on his door and offered him $64,000 more than he was trying to get. Jack listened to Malia a little bit better about faith and willfulness. One thing about Malia's life that Jack admired was that she seemed to be very fortunate. Jack seemed to have to work so hard for things. He thought he should take a lesson from her.

The months went on. Jack continued to talk to Malia regularly, and he even began to go to church. He had found the Newtown Reformed Church and he liked the minister's down to earth sermons. Jack was struggling with trying to have more faith about the same time the divorce agreement was finalized. It gave him peace to turn it over to a Higher Power once he had done all he could do.

The Pennsylvania laws turned out to be fairly exact about the division of property, so Lynn was prevented from "taking everything he owned". During a visit with Lynn to the lawyer's office, Jack outlined the properties that he thought she should own (low maintenance, low risk, high income) and the ones he should own (high maintenance, high risk). He tried to divide them up in such a way to give her the ones that would be easy for her, since she was not experienced as a landlord. Not knowing anything about the properties, Lynn said spitefully "I'll tell you what Jack. You take my list and I'll take yours!"

"OK," said Jack.

Lynn's lawyer took a look at the list and said to Lynn "I wouldn't do that if I were you."

Jack had been giving Lynn most of his paycheck, but in the divorce, the court required him to pay substantially less. Jack thought he was headed for trouble, since Lynn had it in her to try to turn everyone against him. It seemed that divorce always had a negative effect when the standard of living was lowered, and Lynn had quit working, on the advice of her lawyer.

The night after they signed the agreement, Lynn had been very upset. Her standard of living had been much higher than it would be under the divorce agreement even though her lawyer had gotten the maximum amount for her. One night, Jack was on his porch, pondering what to do about the situation. Everyone told him divorce can be very ugly and damaging. Jack didn't really care about money, but Lynn regarded it as essential as food to support her life style. Just then, he heard a booming voice in his head. It was a very loud voice and sounded like Oprah Winfrey. The voice said, "GIVE HER YOUR WHOLE PAYCHECK." Jack JUMPED out of his chair and immediately started countering the voice. He had loud thoughts that said, "WHAT!? She doesn't deserve my whole paycheck! She never lifted a finger to help me on any of these properties! She spent money like water! She ran up the Mastercards! She doesn't deserve it!" Jack was pissed. There's no way he could have that kind of faith!

He called Malia. He told her that God was a black woman, and She had just told him to give Lynn his whole paycheck. Malia laughed and said that he should do what God told him to do. "But what will I live on?" asked Jack.

"God will provide," she said.

"Oh great!" said Jack."Maybe I'm going crazy. This is insane. Do you realize what a big leap of faith this is for me? My father was not there to help me. I bought my own clothes, my own car, and helped support my mother all through school. I paid my own tuition and books. Where was God back then?"

"I'm sure that He ... I mean ... She ... was there somewhere. You came out OK didn't you?" she said.

"OK," he relented."I'll give it a try."

"NO," Malia said emphatically."You don't give it a TRY. You either do it or you don't. There is no such thing as TRYing. Are you going to give her your whole paycheck, or not?"

Jack ended up giving her his whole paycheck. He decided to make a game of it and see if he could make enough extra money to live on. Lo and behold, he was never without money. He was asked to do seminars, he got insurance rebates, and when money was short, things would happen. He would sell one of his properties. He even managed to buy a new car solely on his good credit. The Black Woman took care of him. Along with that, Lynn was afraid to upset him and did not meddle in his relationships. After all, the fool was giving her his whole paycheck and she didn't want to mess that up. One time she mentioned something about his feeling guilty. "What?" said Jack. "You think I am giving you my whole paycheck because I feel guilty? Let me just tell you. I don't feel the least bit guilty for leaving you. In fact, I am really pissed off that your selfishness ruined this marriage." Lynn just looked puzzled. She had no idea why he was doing what he was doing. When he would hand over his signed paycheck to her, she would look at him in awe and wonder what he was living on.

Jack continued his telephone relationship with Malia. Malia talked about Brad and the wedding plans sometimes, but Jack would just be quiet and listen. Jack had no partner in his life to talk about.

One day, Malia mentioned that she would not be able to talk to Jack much longer, because she would be married soon and it wouldn't be proper. She said that she would miss their conversations. It was a surprise moment for Jack. Reality hit him. He might not be able to interact with Malia much longer! His heart sank to the point that he had no defense mechanisms for the strong emotions he was feeling. He told Malia he had to go, but a sob sneaked out before he could stop it. He hung up the phone, and Malia immediately rang him back. He could not pick up the phone in the condition he was in, so he let it ring until his machine answered. He turned off the volume because he couldn't listen to whatever she was going to say. He would have to collect himself before he talked to her again. He never expected to react that way. After all, he knew that it was going to happen. Why was he so upset?

Later that evening, he played back the message. Malia had left a concerned message. "Jack. Jack. Are you there, Jack. Pick up. What's wrong? Jack? ... (then softer) ... Jack."

The next day, Jack looked like hell. Gale stopped by his office and looked in. "Did you stay up late last night and finally get laid? Or, maybe your noodle fell off? God Jack, this looks serious!" She came into his office and closed the door. "OK, my friend," she said, "let's hear it."

Jack went on and on and on. He told Gale how he was so upset, but shouldn't be. He said he had never felt this way before. He told her how everything seemed to be closing in on him. He was so lonely. He thought he had a grip on the Malia thing and he thought he could handle it. It seemed unusual that Gale would sit there and listen for so long without making a crack. Then when he finally was finished and looked up at her. She said, "Life's a bitch, and then you die." Then she got up and left.

She shocked him so much that he rose out of his misery for long enough to see himself feeling so sorry for himself. He howled with laughter. He rang her just as she was getting back to her office and she answered, "Yeah?"

"God, you are a bitch," he said in amused amazement.

"Sure I am," she said. "And when you get done wallowing in self pity, come and see me. Pussyfooting wimp!" Then she hung up.

At lunchtime he entered her office with a flair. "Is the lady ready to go to lunch?" he said sarcastically.

"Sit down, asshole," she barked. She finished up something she was doing on her computer and then spun around in her chair and smiled an obviously fake smile. "You know," she started, "you men amaze me."

"Listen," he said, "If you are not going to tell me something to help, then spare the bullshit."

"I AM going to tell you something that will help. The problem is, will you do what I say? You see, I have helped you already with my womanly advice."

"Oh yeah," he said vehemently, "You suggested lying. That helped, didn't it. Now I am in a situation where my credibility is shot. I can't do anything. I promised I would just be her friend, and that's the way she wants it. Now she is getting married to some Chinese Doctor like she always wanted, and even if I could change her mind, I wouldn't want to ruin her life with the likes of me. I have nothing to offer her. I am financially drained. I am emotionally drained."

"First of all," she said in an uncharacteristically slow and low voice, "I am NOT going to rip your balls off like I would do to anyone else who talked to me that way. Secondly, if you hadn't lied to her, you would have never been with her in the first place. Thirdly, I told you to break your promise to her about calling, and that worked. Fourthly, if you stop falling on your sword with your wimp ass nobility, you would do what I am going to say next. And what I am going to tell you is to get your ass on the next plane to Hawaii and go RUIN her life with the likes of you. And what do you mean you don't have anything to offer her?! You have YOU to offer her. You underrate yourself so much that you really piss me off! I mean it, Jack. If I hear you say another derogatory thing about yourself, I am going to puke on you!" She stood up at her desk and pretended to shove her finger down her throat aiming her mouth at him.

"How can you know this is the right thing to do?" said Jack, "I'll feel like I'm stalking her?"

Gale came around the desk and loomed over him. She pinched his cheek into a grotesque contortion and said, "Get on that f--king plane Jack. Do you hear me Jack? GET ON that f--king plane. You either get on that plane, or you continue to be a wimp-ass co-dependent. You are so codependent that if you died right now, <u>everyone else's</u> life would pass before your eyes. You see, my love, the question to ask is not 'what can you offer her?' The question is 'What can she offer YOU?' People don't get what they **deserve** in this world. They get what they **choose**. So what's it going to be Jack? Do you want her, or not?"

"What if she really doesn't want me now?" said wimp-ass Jack.

"Oh," said Gale, "I think you would learn to live with that. Then it would be a finality. What **I** would have trouble living with is what if she wants you and you DON'T do anything!? I would have trouble living in mediocrity, Jack. What about you?"

After the "talk", Gale and Jack went to lunch. When Jack came back from lunch, he closed the door to his office and started digesting what Gale said. After a time, he decided, "I'm going to go for it!" He started wondering where he was going to get the money. He had no cash flow, and none of his properties were going to closing. Of course, he could take the money out of his paycheck. Nope! He was going to keep the faith.

Just then, his boss Ed came in and dropped a packet on his desk. "Callahan," he said without looking up, "You are going to an educational conference next Monday with IPM International." Jack looked at the plane tickets. Maui! That's the island next to Honolulu! He followed Ed back to his office. "I'm going to Maui?" asked Jack.

"Yes," said Ed matter-of-factly, "and don't pull that shit like last time with the airplane strike!" Ed looked up at him and smirked. "You'll be staying at the Shoreton."

Jack couldn't believe it.

That night he went home and called Malia. She wasn't in. He didn't leave a message. He called her over the next couple of days and she didn't answer. He never left a message because he knew that her father didn't like the idea of her communicating with Jack. He had sent her a planter one time after she was promoted. After the cut flowers were dead, her father had taken the live plants outside in direct sunlight to kill them. Malia told Jack a story once about her father. Malia's brother was supposed to mow the lawn, but could never seem to get the lawn mower started. When Malia's father came home, he could always start the mower. This continued until one day, Malia's Dad came home with a hand push mower. He gave it to Malia's brother and said simply, "Here. This will start."

No. He couldn't really leave a message.

Monday came fast, and Jack still couldn't get Malia on her telephone. He had to go to Maui without contacting her. He figured he would call her when he got there.

After Jack left, Malia called his house. No answer. She tried work. Jack had transferred his calls to Gale's extention.

Gale answered, "IPM, Gale."

"Oh," said Malia, "I was looking for Jack Callahan."

There was a short pause and Gale said, "You must be the Hawaiian Chick."

"I'm Chinese," said Malia.

"Well, I'm a friend of Jack's," Gale said. "He is gone to a seminar for the week."

"So, I guess he has a wife <u>and</u> a 'friend'."

"I'm not that kind of a friend," said Gale, immediately picking up the inference.

"Well, just tell him Malia called."

"Look," started Gale, "this is none of my business, but Jack confides in me and I know him very well."

"Yes?" said Malia, waiting to see what Gale was going to say.

"You've got him all wrong, honey."

There was a bit of silence as Malia was deciding whether she wanted to hear what Gale was going to say next. "How so?" she finally asked.

Gale began, "I have known Callahan for two years. He is the most unpretentious man I have ever known. He told me that he lied to you and what it did to his relationship with you. I guess I feel partly to blame, so I'm going to step in here a little. Remorse and guilt are not fitting with my personality, like with Jack, so I'm not going to apologize, or any of that sh... stuff. But I mean to tell you that I have never seen Jack like this."

"How is he?" asked Malia.

"He is ... well ... not normal. I can't get him interested in any other women. All he does is work and go home. He thinks you know him, and maybe you do, but if you do you are not <u>looking</u> hard enough, or you would see what I see."

"Are you in love with him?"

"I do love the son of a b... gun. In-love? No. He is the best friend a girl could have. And I gotta tell ya, I don't like you very much for hurting my friend. You're hurting yourself too, come to think of it. So, not only don't I like you, but my respect for you is low. So, either way, you are full of rice."

Malia could feel her Korean temper surge, but calmed herself. "Look, Miss Gale. I'm the one who was hurt. I'm the one who lost respect for him."

"You know," said Gale, "That's what happens to people who get hurt. They shut down." Then Gale pretended to be calling out, "If you hurt me, I'm not going to love you!"

Malia whimpered almost inaudibly, "But I do."

There was a momentous silence on Gale's end, then she yelled into the phone, "WHAT! Another pussyfooter. You know, you people drive me nuts. So you are going to marry Brad the Brain Surgeon and you are in love with someone else!"

"He's a neurologist," Malia corrected, not being able to think of a better response.

"Well good," said Gale,"Because it looks to me like you are going to need a brain operation. A Jackobotomy. God, I hope it's not as painful as a gynecological exam. What's wrong with you two? Why can't life be simple?"

"Because of Jack."

"Yes," Gale mumbled, "He does seem to have a knack for complicating things."

Malia sniffled.

"Look honey," Gale said, almost compassionately, "I've been married and divorced twice. The first one was a womanizer and loser. Then I switched to a boring guy who had a good job. I'm probably not the one to give you advice, but if I were you, instead of me, I would be spending my time chasing Jack."

"I'm getting married soon," said Malia.

"Hey! I **can** help you with that one," said Gale proudly. "I left a guy standing at the Altar. Did you ever hear that song, Fifty Ways to Leave Your Lover?"

"I never really paid attention."

"Well, I'll tell ya," said Gale intensely, "It contains some very helpful hints. Listen to it sometime."

"OK, so where is Jack?"

Gale smiled smugly. "He's at the Shoreton in Maui."

"Maui?"

"Yep," said Gale, "Ain't that some sh... coincidence?"

"What should I do?"

"Nobody takes my advice, anyway, but do you really want to know?"

"Well, OK," said Malia, wondering what Gale was going to say now ."

"Spend the night with Doctor Callahan, and call me in the morning, when you feel better."

Malia thanked Gale with mixed emotions, and hung up the phone. He was in Maui! An $80 ticket and half hour plane ride. She felt her excitement ... her passion ... surge. She struggled with it. Should she go? Her Chinese logic told her no: it was over. Her Korean emotions told her to go. What a conflict! She called a disc jockey friend of hers and borrowed Fifty Ways to Leave Your Lover. In the end, her logic relented. After all, she had to erase the doubt nagging at her. She had to see him one more time.

She called a girlfriend in Maui. Her girlfriend said she could visit, and wanted to know, "What was that song playing in the background?"

After arranging to stay with her friend, she called the airlines and scheduled a flight.

Jack was wired when he arrived in Maui. He tried to call Malia, but she still wasn't in. He wasn't worried. He had all week to get her and he couldn't really leave until the seminar was over on Friday. He had taken extra days of vacation to spend in Honolulu, and he was prepared that it might be a lonely stay. He went for a walk outside. He thought about Gale. He really loved her, but she had some crazy ideas. Hell, he was just learning to have faith in a Higher Power, let alone a human being. He walked along the beach and then strolled back to the hotel about seven in the evening. He decided to eat in the hotel and walked into the restaurant. He was led to a table and sat down with the menu. Then he heard a familiar voice call his name, "Jack?"

He turned and there was Malia. Their eyes met and locked as if they had seen each other the day before. They were both speechless for a long time, and then Jack could feel a lump in his throat the size of a grapefruit. He started shaking internally. (Oh God, not now. Whatever was happening to him?) He could not speak. His eyes filled with tears, and he felt like someone who had been away from home for a long time and was just coming back. He had to clench his teeth to keep from chattering. It was all he could do to hold himself together.

Her beautiful voice said "Are you OK, Jack?" (Damn! She could sense his reaction.) All he could do was nod his head affirmatively. Whatever THIS was, he hoped it would pass soon before he made an ass out of himself. She spoke again, "I'm here with my brother's fiancee. We are old friends, and I am visiting her here in Maui. Would you like to join us?"

"N-n no," chattered Jack. "That's OK." He didn't want to embarrass her or take advantage of her hospitality, and he needed time to collect himself.

"Are you staying here at the hotel?" she asked. He nodded. "Are you feeling well?" she asked. He shook his head.

"Actually no," he said. "Maybe I should go." He got up and headed toward the elevator. On the way, his chin started wrinkling with sobs. He could feel her eyes on him as she stood at his table and watched him go.

Jack got to his room and looked in the mirror at himself. "What the hell was that!?" he asked himself, "You are not some teenager. You are too old for this, for God's sake!" He couldn't believe his own reactions. Man! He had never acted like that in his entire life! "She must think I am a real weirdo. Holy s---! I don't understand this!"

Over the next hour, he calmed himself down. Then the phone rang. It was Malia. "Are you OK, Jack?"

"Oh sure," he said, this time more confidently. "I must have caught a bug on the way over. I just got in today."

There was silence on the other end of the phone. Then she said, "You said you wouldn't lie to me anymore, Jack"

Oh God! The lump was back in his throat. Well, he had promised, so he let go. He felt like a little boy. A lonely little boy. He sobbed into the phone "I ... miss you ... so much."

"I'm coming up," she said.

"No...," he said, but she had already hung up the phone.

Then there was a knock at the door. He opened it. He was crying openly, wiping tears and apologetically saying, "I'm really not like this. I'm never like this."

She gave him a compassionate glance and then put her head down. She started walking around the room idly looking at things. There was silence and then she looked at him briefly and longingly. "You know, Jack, I couldn't be with someone who was deceptive."

"Yes, I know."

"And," she continued, "I'm probably not a good Christian because I just couldn't forgive that sort of thing ... as a habit." She walked toward him.

"No," Jack brightened, "not as a habit."

She looked at him as if trying to calculate him. She looked down again and said, "But if I thought it was just someone who slipped one time on a banana peel ..."

Jack finished her sentence. "... and they normally didn't do that sort of thing ... "

"... then, well yes," she continued. "I think I would be more capable of exercising my prerogative as a Christian to forgive if I thought the person ..."

"Wasn't really like that," he finished.

"Yes, but if a certain person wasn't really like that, it would put me in a precarious position because ..."

And he finished, "Because you might realize you had other feelings for this person," said Jack, more confidently, sitting on the couch.

"Exactly!" she said sitting next to him with a worried concerned look. "And some women make a fool out of themselves over and over and lose face with their friends and family."

"But you wouldn't be like that," he said.

"I wouldn't?"

"No because ..."

"... Because," she interrupted, "I am a Chinese woman and we become friends with a man first ... well, maybe it doesn't have to be first (remembering their first night together) and you and I: We have been friends now for a while."

"We have? Yes, we have" realized Jack, still connected with her.

"And we know what to do now," she announced.

"We do? Yes, we do. And what should we do now?" asked Jack quizzically.

"We have to end this relationship," she said simply.

"Oh," said Jack with a bit of shock and pain in his voice.

"Yes," she continued. "This relationship that we are having right now, really sucks." It was out of character for her to say the "S" word.

"It does?" said Jack, now totally confused. "But I thought you were leading up to something else. I mean ... I thought it was going pretty well ..."

"Nope," she interrupted his stammering, "It has to end because I want a new relationship with you."

"Oh," said Jack, feeling better, but with a wondering look in his eyes.

"Yes," she said decisively, "And this one has to different than the one we have now." She took his hand and pulled him over to her. Then she motioned for him to lay his head in her lap and she ran her fingers through his hair and hugged him close at the same time.

"I feel a little confused," he said. She kissed him on the top of his forehead. Then he felt something on the side of his neck. It was ... a tear. He sat up and looked at her. Was it a tear of pity? No. She had a look of confusion and fear ... and yes ... love. There it was, as before. As always. He didn't feel like a little boy anymore. He felt like a man. A man in love. He waited for her to make the first move. It had to be hers.

She moved forward and kissed him. He felt it throughout his entire being. Home again. The world ceased to exist. Time stood still. There was only love, as it was in the beginning and ever shall be. She looked in his eyes and said, "In our new relationship, I want to be able to come home to you. I want to wake up next to you in the morning. I want you there to tickle me when I get too logical. I want to ... I want <u>you</u>, Jack."

"Can you forgive me?" he asked.

"I don't have to. We're even now. I deceived you too."

"You did?"

"Yes, I didn't really come to Maui to visit my friend."

"Then how did you ... ?"

She kissed him again, causing his curiosity to take a low priority.

They didn't make love that night. They didn't need to. Malia felt morally obligated to break her engagement with Brad, first. Just being together was enough. Malia told Jack, "I came here to find out something I already knew. This time my 'logic' came along too. It makes sense now. I know it is right, now."

"Then come home with me," he said smiling. "Come to sunny Pennsylvania with me."

There was a happy silence, and then she committed, "I'll come with you."

The next day she called Brad while Jack was at the seminar. She told Brad she loved him, but was not in-love with him and could not marry him. She called her father to tell him she was going to be moving to Pennsylvania with Jack and she would be bringing Jack home shortly to meet him. He reacted with the longest silence she had ever known him to have. It must have been a fifteen minute silence. She said "Dad! Dad! Are you OK?" He mumbled something inaudible and hung up.

She called her close friends to tell them that she would be

leaving Hawaii with Jack. "Is that the married guy who lied to you?" they asked.

"Yes," she said, "It's him." Of course, they all were in disbelief about the whole situation and were sure she was making a big mistake.

Jack finished his seminar and brought Malia home with him. There were no more obstacles in their way. They lived together until Jack's divorce was final. They traveled to various places in the world and came back to Hawaii to be married. They now live in Paradise, Pennsylvania and have two boys. They have been together ten years now. Jack left the corporate world and became a psychologist as he had always wanted to be. He wrote three books and has become a best-selling author. He hasn't stepped in manure for a long time.

Malia's father stopped killing Jack's plants and has accepted him into the family. Thanks to Jack and Malia, he has two fine grandsons. He has forgiven Jack for not being a Chinese Doctor, for being divorced, and for taking his daughter to Pennsylvania. Malia's brothers decided not to abuse Jack for being indiscriminate with their sister. Jack is grateful for this pardon.

So Jack did meet his soulmate, but not the WAY he thought (ie: not until the WAY he thought was transformed) Can something like this really happen? Well, the following sentence is non-fiction.

Yes.

Dear Reader,

Although I may not be able to <u>answer</u> all correspondence, I am interested in knowing how this book has affected you. I promise I will personally read your letter as I have done for the thousands of people who wrote me about <u>Nasty People</u>. You may write me at:

Dr. Jay
P.O. Box 6048
Wyomissing, PA 19610

or E-mail at SENCARTER@COMPUSERVE.COM

You may also use this address to contact me for **speaking engagements** for your organization, club, or work setting.

Other Books by the Author
Butterflies Don't Land on Manure, by Jay Carter
A fictional book about a man's search for meaning and his transformation. It is filled with humor, adventure, and enlightenment. Filled with modern day dragons and wizards disguised as human beings. A mix of new age, a lasting message, and fun. Men love this book.

Taking the Bully by the Horns; A Children's Version of <u>Nasty People</u>.
After many requests for this book, it was written by Kathy Noll with Dr. Jay Carter. It is for ages 9 thru 15 and contains the principles of the original <u>Nasty People</u> at a childrens level. It provides an understanding of bullies and shows how children can deal with bullies and self esteem. See * -- next page.

Self Analysis; A Kick-Butt Boot-Camp Approach, by Dr. Jay Carter
This is a direct approach to self analysis containing major life-changing principles which come out of the page at you. A collection of the most enlightening bolts and motivating face-slapping principles.

Love, The "L" Word; Refining Tainted Love, by Dr. Jay Carter
Love has become a four letter word in our society. People are afraid to love because of all the things attached to "it". Yet, love is what we are <u>really</u> looking for. We settle for substitutes instead (Drugs, sex, work, etc.), but we can have "it". A very enlightening book. A common comment after reading the book is, "I feel like a thousand pounds has been lifted off my shoulders".

Each book is **$12.95** and $2.55 shipping. The shipping on two books is $4.00. $1.00 shipping for each book after that. To order, clip the coupon below and send to: Unicorn Press (of PA)
                Dept. BD
                P. O. Box 6048
                Wyomissing, PA 19610

Please send me (number) **Taking the Bully** ...(___) **Love** ...(___)

                Self-Analysis ...(___) **Butterflies** ...(___)
Enclosed is $12.95 for each book and $2.55 shipping and handling.

Name   _____ Tele _____

Address _____

        _____ Zip _____

TO ORDER BOOKS by **E-MAIL** with a **CREDIT CARD** ...**TURN PAGE**

TO ORDER BOOKS BY MASTERCARD OR VISA, SEND E-MAIL TO:

sencarter@compuserve.com

Include:
Credit Card Number
Expiration Date
Book Title(s)
Number of Each Title
Total Cost of Books and Shipping Fees

*additional note

"Taking the Bully by the Horns" is a self-help book/web site dedicated to helping children and young teens deal with Bullies/Self-Esteem/Violence. Supported by Schools/Child Orgs/Parents/Doctors, we explore different ways kids are bullied, mentally and physically, how the bully becomes a bully, how the victim becomes a victim, and what can be done about it. Last year, 76.8% of students surveyed said they had been bullied. Fourteen percent experience significant trauma from the abuse. It's time to do something about it.